THE SAGAS OF

Kormák

AND

The Sworn Brothers

THE SAGAS OF
Kormák
AND
The Sworn Brothers

TRANSLATED FROM THE OLD ICELANDIC
WITH INTRODUCTION AND NOTES

By LEE M. HOLLANDER

1949
Princeton University Press
Princeton
For the American-Scandinavian Foundation
New York

PRINTED IN THE UNITED STATES OF AMERICA
BY PRINCETON UNIVERSITY PRESS AT PRINCETON, NEW JERSEY

TO

WILLARD, ELIZABETH, MIRIAM LEE

alls eigi verrfeðrungar

PREFACE

As EVERY translator from the Old Norse knows, it is difficult if not impossible to achieve consistency in the rendering of names; the extremes being, on the one hand, the literal translation of each and every one, and on the other, reproducing all as found. Both are to my mind undesirable. I have therefore in this book attempted the compromise of translating where the English equivalent lay ready at hand, but reproducing others when a translation would have made them unrecognizable to the student consulting the map.

The pronunciation of Old Norse names should not present much difficulty to the reader if he will remember that the acute over vowels signifies length, all not so marked being short, that *ia, io, iu* are rising diphthongs (*ey* may be pronounced like English long *i*), and that the *g* is always "hard." The stress invariably falls on the first syllable.

For general information on the practice of the Skaldic art, of which particularly numerous examples occur in both sagas, the reader is referred to the author's Introduction to *The Skalds* (Princeton University Press for The American-Scandinavian Foundation, 1945).

The book is much the better for the numerous suggestions of Dr. Margaret Schlauch, who went over the entire manuscript. At every stage it has had the benefit of Dr. Leach's circumspection and editorial care. My good friends and colleagues, Robert T. Clark, Jr., and Harry J. Leon, read both Introductions in the proof.

L. M. H.

CONTENTS

Kormák's Saga

The Sworn Brothers' Saga

Contents

Place Names Occurring
in The Sworn Brothers' Saga

Place Names Occurring
in Kormák's Saga

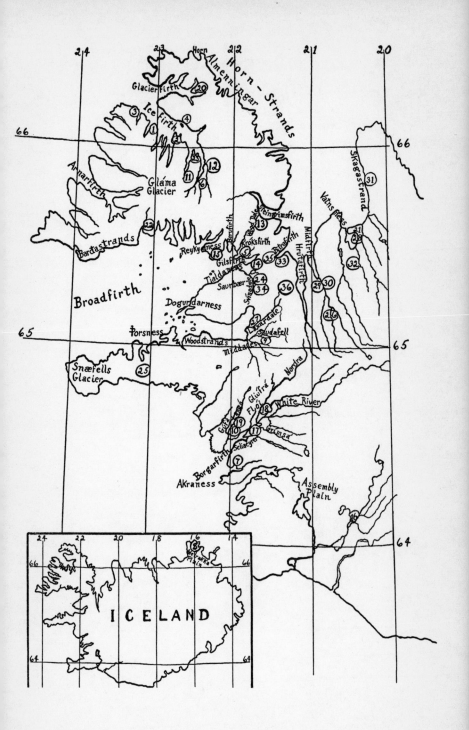

KORMÁK'S SAGA

KORMÁK'S SAGA

INTRODUCTION

REMARKABLE among the sagas of Iceland for the sentimental theme running through it, in an age notably robust, clear-eyed, and unsentimental, is that telling the sad tale of Kormák the skald. Love is not more central in the immortal stories of Romeo and Juliet, of Tristan and Isolde, of Francesca da Rimini, than in Kormák's life and poetry. But it is doubly bitter here in its unfulfillment: in the hero's falling irretrievably in love at first sight and remaining so until death. He is strangely unable—though he unceasingly covets the object of his love and makes life miserable for the two husbands she weds successively, by his constant importunate visits and attentions—to bring himself to accomplish union with her, whether in marriage or otherwise, even when circumstances are favorable and the woman is willing enough.

No other saga so well illustrates the truth of the Old Norse adage that a man's character is his fate: it is Kormák's "problematic" character, compounded essentially of nerveless indecision—at least in the matter of his love for beautiful Steingerd—and explosive rashness, which is the core and substance of this curious saga. There is not a single event in it (barring the Steinvor and Váli episodes, Chaps. XV, XVI) that does not ultimately stem from his unfortunate involvement. At the same time, it is an excellent illustration of the "biographic saga"—one built around a single person and his aberrations like a type case in a psychological novel of our own times. Once we have fathomed the hero's secret, we can follow his doleful fortunes with understanding if not with sympathy.

What, then, can be the explanation of Kormák's abnormal behavior, so much at variance with one of the primal instincts of man? It has set many minds guessing.

The saga says in plain words that Kormák's frustration was due to a spell wrought by the sorceress Thórveig in retaliation for his slaying her two sons (who had waylaid him) and, on top of that, his banishing her from the district. And

Kormák himself affirms this to be the explanation for his conduct.

However, the modern mind seeks some other "more rational" explanation than witchcraft for the teasing problem of Kormák's conduct toward Steingerd. Thus, as we scan the words of the saga carefully, a cynical conclusion might seem indicated, namely, that Kormák became disgusted at the family dickering about the dowry to be given Steingerd by her poorish, or at any rate socially inferior, relatives and impulsively backed out of the whole business. Previously, when Steingerd had asked Kormák to bring his irregular and feud-provoking wooing to a head, he seemed to overcome his dislike for her family, and made the relation "regular" by formally asking her father for her hand in marriage: "The day for the marriage was fixed, and everything was peaceful for a while. But then there were negotiations about the dowry, and differences arose about it. And, strange to say, after all arrangements had been made Kormák seemed no longer interested. And that was because Thórveig brought it about by her witchcraft that Kormák and Steingerd should never have intercourse together" (Chap. VI). Such a cynical view might seem to gain support from the fact that Kormák's widowed mother Dalla, proudly conscious of her high social position, had warned her headstrong and lovestruck son that Steingerd was his inferior.

But this explanation is not in accord with the conventions and views then obtaining. No Old Icelander would have boggled at the massive realities of life in this fashion and for this reason. The best of them haggled, or let their kinsfolk haggle, about the dowry; just as many were shrewd traders who knew how to drive a hard bargain. Nor does this explanation account for Kormák's hesitations to take his own when he meets the twice-wedded Steingerd on his return from abroad, unprotected and (so far as we can discover) complaisant to his advances; and, still less, his refusal to have her when her husband is willing to relinquish Steingerd in his favor.

Similarly, some have fancied that the poet in Kormák rebelled when confronted with "the prose of marriage" and withdrew, fearing lest his erotic illusion about the woman he loved might be shattered by the harsh realities of conjugal life. This explanation, however, also betrays an anachronistic view: poets did not in those times regard themselves as set apart from ordinary mortals. Skalds of genius like Egil, Sigvat, Arnór were, on the contrary, securely married, and others were farmers, traders, warriors who did not feel a clash between their bread-winning occupations and their skald-ship. The modern "artist's incommensurability with life" had no more dawned on them than had the medieval ideal of womanhood.

There is difficulty, likewise, if we go to the other extreme and tentatively offer the grossest explanation at our disposal, physical or psychological impotence caused by an "emotional block" incurred in childhood. Such a suspicion, however, is at once dispelled by the violent outbursts of Kormák's passion-ate jealousy. Moreover, we shall probably not be interpreting too much into stanzas 5 and 6 when we surmise that he had had some little experience with women before meeting Stein-gerd. Still further, the Old Icelanders were notably quick to perceive and rail at the shortcomings and failings of their neighbors; enemies in particular would not have been slow to taunt Kormák, or at least to hint at any disability—if any had been detected. On the contrary, when Steingerd's second husband and his brother wish to cure her of her latent love for Kormák, they impute to him the composition of a most obscene stanza—which they certainly would not have done if they had suspected impotence on his part.

Or—a fourth suggestion—is Kormák the constitutional hesitator, a kind of Old Icelandic Grillparzer, one who is afraid of life and who cannot screw up his courage to the sticking point to wed—or violate—his Kathi, and so drags out a painful and somewhat ridiculous existence in her aura? Hardly. For that, Kormák is too much of a D'Artagnan in all other respects—not at all a flaccid esthete but a ruthless, hard-handed, quarrel-seeking fighter who does not hesitate to maim and kill his opponents.

A psychologist might be inclined to suggest a Freudian complex, such as a mother-tie. But that desperate explanation, again, fails to meet the facts of the case: Kormák does not seem to get along any too well with his mother, whom, by the way, he resembles in physical appearance. Also—a point to emphasize—Steingerd, the pronounced blonde, is of a type radically different from Dalla. Besides, as hinted above, Kormák is not unacquainted with women, aside from Steingerd.

So we would seem to be thrown back on the saga's own insistent explanation—that Kormák's behavior is due to witchcraft. In other words, the magic curse is the sufficient and tangible cause around which the fable is built, its central motif: it will not do for us to make light of the supernatural causation. Now very probably we may assume that in every case of supernaturalism we shall find it coupled with, or shall we say actuated by, the power of suggestion; which provides us with still another, and to the writer acceptable, cue to Kormák's behavior.

In the saga, Kormák meets with magic first, and most fatally, in the encounter with the witch Thórveig. It is she who speaks the curse which is to destroy his happiness forever. At the time, he professes not to believe in her power: "That you shall not be able to bring about, you evil hag," he says when the curse is pronounced. But after it does take effect and Kormák so mysteriously fails to accomplish the union he had so ardently wished, he is ready to acknowledge its power.

And, to repeat, when his brother gently twits him for always reverting to Steingerd in his mournful stanzas but not wanting to marry her when he had the chance, Kormák retorts: "More was this the work of ill wights than due to my own waywardness" (Chap. XVIII). He evidently believes in magic now.

In another encounter with occult powers, Kormák behaves in a typically "contrary" fashion, betraying his own uncertainty. His mother prevails upon him to borrow for his duel with Bersi the old magic sword Skofnung from a trusted supporter of the family. This sword is exceedingly tempera-

mental and needs to be handled in a most particular way to
conserve its virtues and to have it give victory. Kormák re-
ceives the directions for its care with abuse and scorn, then
willfully disregards them, with the result, we are to understand, that in the *holmgang* he wounds himself and thus loses
out (Chaps. IX, X). His very braggadocio in this instance,
his behaving as though he did not need supernatural help, and
was just humoring his mother, would seem to show that he
half and half believes in the magic power of Skofnung: "he
doth protest too much."

Later, when Kormák and his brother are about to cast off
in order to sail for Norway, "a walrus emerged close to the
ship's side. Kormák hurled his spear at it—it struck home
and the animal dived out of sight. People thought they recognized the witch Thórveig's eyes in it. . . ." This is a common enough motif in the sagas, but the point is that Thórveig
and her evil designs are on Kormák's mind—that the suggestion of her powers is working in him.

On still another occasion, Kormák, again on his mother's
insistence, consults another wise-woman, Thórdís, in order
to solicit her aid in an impending duel with Thorvard, the
brother of Steingerd's husband. Thorvard had been to see her
before, on the same errand; but Thórdís promises to do her
best, nevertheless, and render Kormák's body, like his opponent's, invulnerable to iron. This she does, although Kormák
surprises her in the magic act (which is against the rules).
Thereupon she volunteers to free him of the love curse by
some hocus-pocus, slaughtering her geese for the purpose.
But Kormák, pretending sleep, peeks again and so frustrates
her labors. When scolded by her he replies defiantly, "I don't
believe in this kind of thing." Yet after the duel, in which he
overcomes his opponent only by main strength, crushing his
ribs with a sword blow, Kormák speaks a stanza acknowl-
edging that the witch-woman *had* blunted his sword so that
it was not reddened with blood. In other words, we may say
that Kormák's *intellect* refuses to believe in witchcraft but
that his *mind* is suggestible to it.

All other persons in the saga are but a foil to Kormák, with the possible exception of Bersi, who interests the narrator to such an extent that he is carried away beyond Bersi's involvement with Kormák through Steingerd, to a time far beyond the span of Kormák's life. Bersi is just about the opposite of Kormák in character while more than his match as a ruthless fighter, besides being a good skald. Kormák knows better than to molest Steingerd while she is in Bersi's keeping. Frank, open-hearted, straightforward, steadfast, it was Bersi's mistake to believe Narfi and the Thorkels, father and son, who say that Kormák is no longer interested in Steingerd; and a similar misjudgment and generous complaisance leads him to marry the vixen Thórdís. Though unaggressive he knows how to hit back with fearful determination and executes his vengeance against Thórarin and his sons and against his brother-in-law Váli in a perfectly cold-blooded way. We cannot, any more than the narrator, deny him our sympathy as a man of indomitable spirit and a generous heart—a sterling character for his times.

Unfortunately, the saga allows us to discern the character of Steingerd but indistinctly. Timorous and overly conventional she is not; we may even detect a streak of coarseness in her treatment of Bersi, whom she, to be sure, had married against her will. On the other hand, one may discover a certain tenderness in her relation to the weak and good-natured Thorvald while yet she is ever fascinated by Kormák's brilliance and daring. If we read between the lines we may guess a natural exasperation on her part when in his encounter with her on the heath Kormák incomprehensibly fails to make free of her love; may, in fact, surmise that her angry exclamation next morning, "The devil take you and your gold," reveals her resentment of his forgetting—as one author delicately puts it—that his inamorata has not only a soul but also a body. If so, that would not discredit her in our eyes.

Little can be, or needs be, said about such subsidiary characters as Thorkel, Steingerd's irascible and irresolute father; Narfi, the stereotype half-knave, half-fool; Steinar, grim old swashbuckler; Thorgils, Kormák's cool-headed and gentle-minded brother.

For one familiar with the Icelandic sagas, it would seem ironical that a story so full of psychological interest should have been told so crudely and haltingly, in such a harsh, angular, often staccato, style sometimes bordering on incomprehensibility, and with so many patent contradictions and repetitions of motif—almost absent-mindedly, as it were. To account for this, it has been assumed rather generally that, in contrast with the vast majority of other sagas, there was no local tradition about Kormák and that the saga was built up around the unusually numerous verses by him (and Bersi).

On that assumption, however, it would be difficult to explain the preservation, in fairly orderly arrangement, of these verses. Furthermore, such an assumption does not tally either with the fact that the prose frequently contradicts the pertinent stanza where a misunderstanding of the latter is out of the question, or with the existence of important passages for which no counterpart is found in the stanzas. So one has to reckon with a tradition, however slender. But the weightiest consideration speaking against secondary origin is the total absence, both in the style and in the tone of the love story, of any such southern, "romantic" influences as are clearly discernible in later sagas like those of the Laxdœlers, of Hallfred, of Gunnlaug; that, on the contrary, Kormák's saga is remarkable for its complete unawareness of Christianity, its thoroughly heathen motivations, the abundance of native supernaturalism.

Indeed, all these considerations speak for a very early origin, say, the first years of the thirteenth century. In fact, much would seem to point to a direct taking down from dictation—possibly from the story of some narrator not yet skilled in the inimitable, though almost stereotyped, elegance and incisiveness acquired by saga tellers (or writers) in the next succeeding generations; to them it would have been an easy matter to reduce the style to regularity and to eliminate the contradictions and repetitions that now mar the saga. The real wonder is that this was not done.

As the saga stands, the narrator appears to take for

granted, on the part of his hearers, a knowledge of the locale and of the great families of northern Iceland. Certainly for an Icelander he seems unusually indifferent to genealogical lore and has abnormally little to say about such powerful and famous chieftains as Bersi, Olaf Pá, Midfirth-Skeggi. On the other hand, he *is* interested in the lore and practices of olden times, and keenly so in skaldship, for he has preserved for us some of the best as well as the earliest erotic verse of Old Germanic times.

Here it is important to bear in mind that the very existence of erotic poetry at this time and under such adverse conditions as the North then offered, is astonishing in itself. In the middle of the tenth century—Kormák was born about 945 and died about 975—a "romantic" interest in woman, the "chivalry" distinguishing the upper classes in the high Middle Ages, was not yet remotely felt there. Nor can there be any thought of classical or oriental impulses, which must be reckoned with in accounting for the rise of the earliest Provençal lyrics.

There were not in the North, and more particularly so in Iceland, the profound social cleavages that marked the feudal age in Central and Southern Europe and that provided the social tensions and the background for the cultivation of erotic poetry. After all, there were only farmers, some prosperous and "of good old stock," others poor—the slaves did not count. In the case of Kormák, as in fact also in the cases of later erotic poets like Hallfred and Gunnlaug, the kinsfolk on either side would have been satisfied with the lovers' marrying; whereas, in accordance with the mores then prevailing, any familiarity with the person of the girl, real or implied in amorous verse, was bitterly resented as harmful to her reputation and hence to the whole clan. Severe laws sought—unsuccessfully—to restrict the output of such verse. Thus conditions were as unpropitious as possible for the development of erotic poetry. The real wonder is that there was any.

Again, for the expression of their romantic feelings, the skalds chose the inflexible mold of the *dróttkvætt*[1]—a form

---

[1] For an account of the *drottkvætt* measure, cf. Hollander, *The Skalds*, 9 f.

which, however admirably suited to pompous eulogiums of
kings and their martial deeds, seems to us a harsh manacle
for the more playful sentiments or the passionate outbursts
of love. Certainly the elaborate apparatus of plural kennings
that goes with this art form was not propitious for the expression of genuine feeling. Hence it is not surprising that
but little of this verse can measure up to the medieval lyric
at its best.

As for Kormák, who, for aught we know, may have been
the first to use the *dróttkvætt* for gentler themes, we must in
all fairness remember that he preceded the earliest trouba-
dours by centuries. Even so, it would be a mistake to rate his
poetry too highly. Though fiery, his imagination does not
succeed in melting the stiff, heavy medium and molding it to
his own image. Indeed, his language is at times curiously
threadbare, his numerous kennings, for the most part, frigid
and repetitious. The woman of his love is the *Hlín* of this or
the *Gefn* of that. Only in a few stanzas does he transcend the
stereotype of the Skaldic manner and become truly poetic.
The arch stanzas about the worth of Steingerd, the roman-
tically passionate hyperbole that rocks will float and the
mountains plunge into the sea before the like of her is born
into the world, the strikingly suggestive stanza about the
surging and ebbing of the waves with their flotsam and jet-
sam—these, to be sure, strike notes that are rarely heard in
Old Germanic poetry. If we had more verse of the same power
and intensity, Kormák's rank among the great skalds would be
more secure. Many of the other stanzas are of high quality—
as are those of Bersi—but not outstanding. Nor can the fragments of Kormák's *drápa* on the Norwegian Earl Sigurd
change this evaluation.

Technically, Kormák's verse clearly belongs with the pre-
ceding age rather than with the succeeding one. There is still
considerable freedom in many of his stanzas in respect to the
niceties of rhyme and the number of syllables of *dróttkvætt*;
and rhythmically his lines are fairly monotonous. There is no
hint, whether in the content of his stanzas or his often exceedingly complicated kennings, of the revolution to be
brought about by Christianity a generation later.

Our saga, together with a dozen others, is handed down in the manuscript codex called *Möðruvallabók*, which was compiled toward the middle of the fourteenth century. Two pages of another parchment (AM 162 fol.) and a number of paper manuscripts differ so inconsiderably from it that we may safely assume that they are all derived from the same original.

The present translation has had the benefit of the excellent new edition by Einar Ól. Sveinsson in the great *Fornritafélag* collection (1939), as well as of that by Moebius (1886), the introduction and notes of which still are valuable. With regard to the frequently very difficult stanzas, the work of E. A. Kock (now made more easily available in his *Den Norsk-Isländska Skaldedigtningen*, 1948) has been revolutionary. In the main, the translation of the verse is based on his interpretations.

I · KORMÁK'S PARENTAGE

KING HAROLD FAIRHAIR ruled over Norway[1] when the events here told took place. At that time there lived in the kingdom a chieftain called Kormák,[2] whose kin lived in the district of Vík,[3] a man rich and of noble birth. He was a man of great valor and had been with King Harold in many battles. His son was called Ogmund. He was a youth of great promise, big and strong at an early age. As soon as he was of sufficient age and strength, he went on viking expeditions in summer, but stayed with the king in winter. He made himself a name and acquired much wealth.

One summer he went on a viking expedition to the west. There he encountered a man called Ásmund. He was a man of great prowess and had overcome many a viking and warrior. They learned of each other's whereabouts, and word went between them. Then they met and arranged where the fight should be, and fought one another. Ásmund had the greater force (of ships) but did not use all in the battle. They fought for four days. Many in Ásmund's company fell, and he himself fled; but Ogmund won the victory and returned home with fame and much wealth.

Kormák declared that Ogmund was not likely to win more fame in forays, "and I shall get you for wife Helga, the daughter of Earl Fródi."

"I am agreeable to that," said Ogmund.

Then they journeyed to Earl Fródi. He made them welcome, and they presented their errand. The earl was favorable to it although he considered there was something outstanding in Ogmund's dealings with Ásmund. Yet the offer was accepted. Father and son returned home, and the marriage feast was arranged for. A great many people came to it. Earl Fródi's daughter Helga had a foster-mother who had second sight. She went along with her.

The viking Ásmund learned about these happenings. He came to meet Ogmund and challenged him to single combat. Ogmund accepted the challenge. Helga's foster-mother was wont to feel over the body of men before they went to

battle. She did so with Ogmund before he left home. She
foretold that no great harm would come to him. Then both
went to the holm[4] and fought together. The viking aimed a
blow at Ogmund's side, but his sword did not cut. Thereupon
Ogmund quickly raised his sword and shifted it to the other
hand and hewed off Ásmund's leg and took from him three
marks of gold as a release from the holm.

II · OGMUND SETTLES IN ICELAND

ABOUT that time King Harold Fairhair died, and Eric
Bloody-Axe succeeded him.[1] But Ogmund did not make
friends of Eric and (his mother) Gunnhild and readied his
ship to sail to Iceland. Ogmund had a son by Helga whose
name was Fródi. When the ship was about to sail, Helga fell
sick and died, and so did their son Fródi. Then they sailed
out to sea, and Ogmund cast his high-seat pillars[2] overboard.
The ship made land at the Midfirth, and his high-seat pillars
had drifted on shore there before he arrived. There they
dropped anchor.

At that time Skeggi, called Midfirth-Skeggi,[3] was chieftain
of that district. He rowed out to them and invited them to
come into the firth and offered them land for settlement. Ogmund accepted this and measured off the ground for a house.
It was the belief at that time that if the measuring rod grew
smaller, when used repeatedly, the fortunes of the man using
it would also diminish, but would thrive if the rod increased
in size.[4] The rod grew smaller although they tried it three
times. Then Ogmund had a house built there on the gravel
banks and lived there from that time on. He married Dalla,
the daughter of Onund sjóni (the seer). Their sons were
Thorgils and Kormák. Kormák was dark-haired, with curls,
and his skin was of a light color.[5] He resembled his mother
somewhat; he was big and strong and of an aggressive disposition. Thorgils was taciturn and gentle. When the brothers
were grown up, Ogmund died. Dalla managed the farm with

the help of her sons. Thorgils carried on the farm work under the supervision of Midfirth-Skeggi.

III · KORMÁK FALLS IN LOVE WITH STEINGERD

THORKEL was the name of a man who lived at Tunga (The Tongue). He was married, and his daughter's name was Steingerd. She was being fostered at Gnúpsdale farm. One fall a whale was stranded on Vatnsness. It belonged to the two brothers, the sons of Dalla. Thorgils offered Kormák the choice whether he preferred to go to the mountains (to bring in the sheep) or to the whale (to flense it). He chose to go to the mountains with the servants.

A man called Tósti was the overseer and was to manage the gathering of the sheep. He and Kormák rode to the farm at Gnúpsdale, and there they stayed overnight. A big hall was there, and fires were lit for the men (for them to sit by). In the evening Steingerd left the women's quarters,[1] together with a maid. From the hall[2] they heard the voices of men not known to them.

The handmaid said: "Steingerd dear, let's look and see what guests have come."

Steingerd said there was no need to; yet she went to the door and stood upon the threshold to peep above the wood stack(?). There was a space between the shutter and the threshold, and there her feet showed.[3] Kormák saw them and spoke this verse:

> 1. Raging love arose my
> ravished heart within, when
> under panel peeped her
> pretty ankles, just now:
> will these feet, I fear me,
> fair one, later put me—
> or I know not ought of
> armlet-Friggs[4]—in danger.

When Steingerd noticed that she was seen, she slipped into the passageway and looked from under Hagbard's beard.[5] There, the light shone on her face.

Then Tósti said: "Kormák, do you see those eyes outside by the Hagbard-head?" Then Kormák spoke this verse:

> 2. Brightly beamed the lights-of
> both-her-cheeks[6] upon me—
> e'er will I recall it—
> o'er the heaped-up wood-pile;
> and the instep saw I
> of the shapely woman—
> no laughing matter, lo! my
> longing—by the threshold.

And again:

> 3. Brightly shone the beaming
> brow-moons[7] of the goodly
> lady linen-dight, how
> like a hawk's, upon me;
> but that beam from forehead's-
> bright-hued-orbs, I fear me,
> of the Eir[8]-of-gold doth
> ill spell for me later.[9]

Tósti said: "She is looking hard at you."
Kormák spoke this verse:

> 4. Lifted ne'er—my love I
> likewise hid not—an eye from
> me the ring-dight maid; in
> mind she always dwelleth—
> when that, on threshold standing,
> thence—I'll not forget it—
> steadfast on me Steingerd
> stared by the neck of Hagbard.[10]

Then the women went into the hall and sat down. Kormák overheard what they said about his appearance. The hand-maid thought Kormák swart and ugly; but Steingerd declared him to be handsome in all respects, "except for one blemish—the hair curls on his forehead."

Then Kormák spoke this verse:

5. Blemish on my body
bore I one, at dusk the
lady linen-dight—though
little—told her handmaid:
said the Hlín-of-whitest-
hawkland[11] that my hair was
—well I know the ways of
women—curled on forehead.

The maid said: "His eyes are black, sister, and that is ill becoming to him."

Kormák heard that and spoke this verse:

6. Black eyes boast I, necklace-
bearer,[12] in thy presence;
also am I, Ilm[13]-of-
armrings, pale and sallow;
yet remember I many a
maiden's kiss and converse,
welcome with comely women as
Kormák, handsome fellow!

They stayed there that night. The next morning when Kormák arose he went to the water-butt to wash himself. Then he went to the sitting room. He saw no one there, but heard voices in an inner room and stepped in. There he found Steingerd with her women.

The handmaid said to Steingerd: "Here that handsome man comes now, Steingerd."

She replied: "Indeed he bears himself handsomely." Steingerd was combing her hair.

Kormák said: "Will you lend me your comb?" Steingerd handed it to him. She had wonderful hair, fair and long.

The maid said: "You would surely give a great deal if your wife had hair such as Steingerd has, or such eyes."

Then Kormák spoke this verse:

7. Either eye, faith! in the
   ale-breweress' face is
   worth to me in wadmal,
   wench, fully three hundreds;[14]
   on her head the hair the
   Hlín-of-rings[15] is combing—
   I hold it worth five hundred:
   high she comes, I reckon!

The maid said: "You are fond enough of each other; so (I suppose) you would put a steep price on her whole person." Then Kormák spoke this verse:

8. Well considered, the woman's
   worth the whole of Iceland—
   heavy though my heart—of
   Hunland,[16] and of Denmark;
   not for all of England's
   earth and kingdoms I'd fore-
   go the golden-braided
   girl, ay, nor yet for Ireland.

Now Tósti entered and asked Kormák to attend to something. Kormák spoke this verse:

9. Let my horse light-footed—
   lash it!—bear you swiftly,
   tired Tósti, o'er the
   trackless heath, unwearied;
   fitting far more is it
   for me now to talk with
   shapely maid than shoo the
   sheep in mountain pastures.

Tósti said that would (indeed) seem more entertaining to Kormák. He went his way, and Kormák sat down for a game of tables (with her) and entertained himself well. Steingerd said that he spoke better than she had been told he did. He sat there all day. Then he spoke this verse:

10. To me, cleansed, there came with
comb the Freya[17]-of-the-
hair-shaft :[18] warm the welcome
was to skald then given,
little known—but lasting
love I bear the Eir[19]-of-
golden-girdle—though the
guest was to the woman.

Then Tósti came back from the mountains and both returned home.

From that time on, Kormák made it his custom to go to
Gnúpsdale to visit Steingerd, and he asked his mother to
make him fine clothes so that Steingerd should find him attractive. Dalla said that there was a great social difference
between them; also, that she was not sure whether all would
go well if Thorkel in Tunga heard of it.

IV · KORMÁK PUNISHES NARFI

THORKEL soón learned what was going on and considered
it a dishonor to him and to Steingerd if Kormák did not come
to a firm agreement about it. He sent for Steingerd, and she
returned home to him.

Narfi was the name of a man who lived with Thorkel—a
self-assertive and foolish fellow, boastful and not of much
account. Narfi said to Thorkel: "If Kormák's visits here dis-
please you, I can tell you right quickly what to do about it."
Thorkel said he would follow his advice.

In the fall Narfi attended to the slaughtering. One time
Kormák came to Tunga. He saw Steingerd in the kitchen.
Narfi was standing by a kettle, and when the sausages were
done he lifted out one and held it under Kormák's nose and
spoke this verse:

11. How would seem, Kormák, to you
these kettle-worms?[1]

Kormák replied:

> 12. Good doth seem the suet boiled
>   to the son of Ogmund.[2]

And in the evening, when Kormák made ready to go home, he saw Narfi and remembered his mocking words.

Kormák said: "I am thinking, Narfi, that I shall sooner give you a beating rather than you shall have a say about my goings and comings."

And he dealt him a blow with the hammer of his axe and spoke this verse:

> 13. What, unwise snath-Áti,[3]
>   ails thee, food to mention?
>   What need, Narfi, for this
>   nerviness toward me?

And again:

> 14. Asked the nosey knave, the
>   neats who feedeth, how I—
>   red the lubber's lids were—[4]
>   liked his suet sausage.
>   Had the sooty-slouch-of
>   seamy-tatters,[5] he who
>   dumps the dung on homefields,
>   a dog's beating from me.

V · KORMÁK SLAYS THÓRVEIG'S SONS. HER CURSE

THÓRVEIG was the name of a woman. She was a great witch. She lived at Steinsstead[1] in the Midfirth district. She had two sons. The older one was called Odd, the younger one, Gudmund, and both were overbearing men. Odd made it his habit to go to Tunga to visit Thorkel and to talk with Steingerd. Thorkel got to be on very familiar terms with the brothers and egged them on to ambush Kormák. Odd said that would not be too great a task for them.

One day, Kormák came to Tunga. Steingerd was in the living room, sitting on the dais.[2] The sons of Thórveig also sat in the hall, all ready to fall upon Kormák when he entered. Thorkel had fastened a bare sword on one side of the door, and Narfi a scythe with a long handle on the other. Now when Kormák came in by the hall door, the scythe fell down from above and hit the sword, making a big notch in it. Then Thorkel came up and said that Kormák was doing a lot of mischief, and used much violent language. Then he turned quickly back into the room, calling on Steingerd to go with him. They left by the other door, and then Thorkel locked her in an outside storehouse and said that she and Kormák were never to see one another again. Kormák went into the room, swifter than they (the brothers) had expected, and they were caught by surprise. Kormák looked all around but did not see Steingerd but only the brothers who were whetting their swords. He turned away abruptly and spoke this verse:

15. Rang the scythe 'gainst Hrungnir's-
round-foot-rest,[3] what time I
in had gone the armlet's-
Ilm[4] in hall to visit:
worse it will be for you,
warrior, if you threaten
ill to me—the ale-of-
Ygg[5] will hardly fail me.[6]

And not finding Steingerd anywhere Kormák spoke this verse:

16. Gone now is the girl for
good; yet notwithstanding—
what else in the hall here?—
I harbor love for Steingerd;
high and low I hunted,
her to find with brow-rays[7]—
eager for her am I
ever—through the household.

Then Kormák went to the house in which Steingerd was and forced it open and talked with her.

She said: "You behave carelessly, trying to speak with me; for the sons of Thórveig are set to kill you."

Then Kormák spoke this verse:

17. Sword-whetting, the twain sit there,
    sons of a churl, within doors—
    foemen both, who fain would
    fell me if 'twere fated.
    Howbeit, if on heath they
    had at me—rather could two
    suckling lambs assail a
    savage wolf than they me!

Kormák sat there throughout the day. Then Thorkel saw that his plans had miscarried, and he asked the sons of Thórveig to waylay Kormák in a certain dale outside his farm.

Then Thorkel said: "Narfi is to go with you, but I shall stay at home and come to your help if you should need me."

In the evening Kormák left Steingerd to go home, and as soon as he came to that dale he saw three men and spoke this verse:

18. Cower men[8] to keep me
    from the comely Gná[9]-of-jewels:
    sooner said than done, to
    sunder me from Steingerd;
    all the more, the more they
    make me shun her, shall I
    go to see the Gefn[9]-of-
    golden-rings, and love her.[10]

Then the sons of Thórveig jumped up and fought with Kormák for a long time. Narfi sneaked about on the outside. Thorkel saw from his house that the brothers were not making much progress, and seized his weapons. At that moment Steingerd came out and saw what her father intended to do and held on to him so that he could not get away to help them. The end of the matter was that Odd fell and Gudmund was disabled and died later. Thereupon Kormák returned home, and Thorkel looked after the brothers.

Thereafter Kormák went to see Thórveig and told her that he did not care for her to stay in the Midfirth district.

"You shall remove yourself at the time I determine, and I shall deny you any redress for your sons."

Thórveig replied: "Likely enough that you succeed in making me move from the district, with my sons unatoned for; but I shall pay you back and tell you that you will never have Steingerd."

Kormák said: "You will not have the power to do that, you evil old hag."

VI · KORMÁK WINS STEINGERD'S HAND BUT FAILS TO APPEAR AT THE MARRIAGE

THEREAFTER Kormák went to visit Steingerd as before. And one time when they spoke about these happenings she expressed herself as quite pleased.

Kormák spoke this verse:

> 19. Cower men to keep thy
>   countenance hidden from me;
>   too weak they are to win in
>   weapon-thing-meet[1] o'er me:[2]
>   rather will all rivers
>   run uphill in Iceland
>   than, golden-trinkets'-Gefn,[3] I
>   give thee o'er unfought for.

"Don't say so much about that," said Steingerd; "there is many a thing might balk you."

Then Kormák spoke this verse:

> 20. Whom would'st, Steingerd, have as
>   husband, among warriors?—

> seeing thou, Hlín-of-silken-
> snoods,[3] look'st at me kindly.[4]

Steingerd replied:

> 21. Fródi's brother,[5] blind e'en,
> breaker-of-rings,[6] would I
> have as husband: if the
> heavenly powers willed it.[7]

Kormák said: "Now you chose the man you should; many a time have I come here to see you."

Then Steingerd asked Kormák to make friends with her father and marry her. And for Steingerd's sake Kormák gave Thorkel valuable presents. Then a good many people took hold of the matter, and the upshot of it was that Kormák asked Steingerd in marriage and that she was betrothed to him. The day for the marriage was fixed and everything was peaceful for a while. But then there were negotiations about the dowry, and differences arose about it. And, strange to say, after all arrangements had been made Kormák seemed no longer interested. And that was because Thórveig brought it about by her witchcraft that Kormák and Steingerd should never have intercourse together.

Thorkel in Tunga had a grown son also called Thorkel, with the nickname Toothgnasher. He had been abroad for some time. That summer he returned to Iceland and lived with his father. Kormák did not come to the marriage on the day agreed upon, and the time agreed upon went by without his coming. This seemed an insult to Steingerd's kinsmen, for him to break off the match, and they discussed among themselves what was to be done.

VII · STEINGERD IS MARRIED OFF TO BERSI

BERSI[1] was the name of a man who lived on the farm of Saurbær[2] (Fen Farm), a wealthy man and noble-hearted, a great fighter, accustomed to go on the holm. He had been married to Finna the Fair, but she was deceased at this time. Ásmund was the name of their son, a youth then but mature for his age. Bersi's sister was called Helga. She was unmarried as yet, of good appearance, and an excellent manager. She had conducted the household after Finna's death. On the farm called Múli[3] (Headland) there dwelled a man called Thórd the son of Arndís. He was married to Thórdís, the sister of Bork the Stout.[4] They had two sons, both younger than Ásmund, the son of Bersi. Another man was called Váli. His farm was called Válastead. It is situated not far from the Hrútafirth.[5]

Thórveig the witch went to see Holm-Bersi and told him her troubles—that Kormák had forbidden her to live in the Midfirth district. Bersi bought her some land west of the Hrútafirth, and she lived there for a long time afterwards.

One time when Thorkel in Tunga and his son spoke about Kormák's breach of promise they thought they should avenge themselves. Narfi said: "I have a plan which will work. Let us ride west with our wares and go to Saurbær to visit Bersi. He is a widower. And let us involve him in our cause by marriage. We can depend on him altogether."

This plan they adopted and rode till they came to Bersi in Saurbær. He welcomed them in. In the evening they got to talk about who were good matches among women.

Narfi said that there was none as good as Steingerd, "and many a one thinks she would suit you well, Bersi."

He replied: "I have heard it said that there was a hitch in that, though the match be a good one otherwise."

Narfi said: "If men are afraid of Kormák, there is no need to be, because he is completely out of the question in this business."

And when Bersi heard that he took the matter up and asked Thorkel (Toothgnasher) for the hand of Steingerd. He answered favorably and betrothed his sister to him. They were to ride north, eighteen men altogether, to celebrate the marriage. Thórd Arndísarson went along with Bersi.

A man was called Vígi,[6] big and strong and skilled in magic. He was a kinsman of Bersi's and he came along with him. They placed great reliance on Vígi. His farm was at Holm. Only picked men went along on this journey. And when they arrived in the north at Thorkel's farm it was arranged that no news about the wedding should be spread in the district. This was done much against Steingerd's wishes. The sorcerer Vígi inquired into the business of everyone who came to the farm or wished to leave it. He seated himself near the door of the hall and also slept there.

Now Steingerd had Narfi called to her, and when he came she said: "Kinsman, I want you to tell Kormák about the arrangements which are being made here about my marriage. I want you to go on this errand to him."

Then Narfi left the farm stealthily, but when he had got but a short way Vígi came after him and told him to get himself straight home and not try any trickery. Both returned and the night passed. In the morning, Narfi tried again, but did not get as far as in the evening, because Vígi lay in wait for him and drove him back relentlessly.

When the marriage feast was over the company made ready to leave. Steingerd had (her) gold and valuables with her. Then they rode to the Hrútafirth in rather leisurely fashion. Narfi set out as soon as they had left and arrived at Mel. Kormák was building a wall and beating it fast with a rammer.[7] Narfi carried his shield as he rode up and pretended to be at ease but let his eyes roam about uneasily like those of a hunted beast.[8] Some men were up on the wall with Kormák when Narfi arrived. His horse backed up. He was girded with a sword.

Kormák said: "What tidings, Narfi? Did you have guests over night?"

Narfi replied: "There is little news to report, but guests we had plenty."

Kormák said: "Who all were the guests?"

Narfi said: "Holm-Bersi with seventeen others, and he celebrated his wedding."

Kormák asked: "Who was the bride?"

"Bersi was married to Steingerd, Thorkel's daughter," said Narfi, "and she sent me here to tell you the news."

Kormák said: "There is always ill in your speech." Kormák sprang at Narfi and struck him on his shield, and when the shield was knocked against Narfi he was slightly wounded on his chest and fell from his horse; but the horse ran away with his shield. Kormák's brother Thorgils said that Kormák carried things too far. Kormák replied that he got what he deserved.

Narfi came to again, and they spoke together. Thorgils asked: "Who all was at the marriage feast?" Narfi told him. "Did Steingerd know of this before?"

Narfi said: "Not before the same evening when people came to the feast." Narfi told about his encounters with Vígi and said that in all likelihood it would be easier for Kormák to whistle after Steingerd and make a fool of him—Narfi—than to fight with Bersi.

Then Kormák spoke this verse:

22. Hero, hold on tight to
     horse, and buckler also:
     swift and sudden my rammer
     smites thee on the temple.
     Say thou ne'er since, though of
     seven a day thou hearest,
     breaker-of-cairns,[9] of banquets—;
     a boil thou hast on forehead.

Thorgils asked about the marriage agreements between Bersi and Steingerd. Narfi said that Steingerd's kinsmen now were freed from all difficulty about her marriage, however it turned out, and that Bersi and his son alone were responsible for it.

VIII · KORMÁK VAINLY PURSUES BERSI

KORMÁK seized his horse, his weapons, and the saddle harness.

Thorgils asked: "What are you about now, brother?"
Kormák spoke this verse:

23.   Bersi brazenly has
      borne away—forsooth the
      anger has he earned of
      Ygg's-friend[1]—my beloved,
      her who me loved most, the
      maiden of sad mien—all
      day I dallied with my
      darling, kissing her often.

Thorgils said: "That is a rash course to take, because Bersi
will probably have reached his homestead before you catch up
with him. However, I shall ride with you."

Kormák said he would go and wait for no one. He mounted
his horse right away and galloped off as fast as he could.
Thorgils quickly collected a company and got eighteen men
together. They caught up to Kormák on the Hrútafirth Ridge.
Kormák by that time had quite winded his horse. They
turned in the direction of Thórveig's farm. Then they saw
that Bersi had got one of Thórveig's boats.

Thórveig had said to Bersi: "I wish you would accept a
small gift from me, with my good wishes."

It was a small round shield edged with iron. Thórveig said
that she expected that Bersi would not be wounded if he protected himself with it.

"But it is a gift of trifling value compared with your procuring me this dwelling."

Bersi thanked her for her gift, and then they parted.

Thórveig got some men to bore holes in all the boats along
the shore, because she knew beforehand that Kormák and his
men would come there. Soon after, Kormák and his company
arrived and asked Thórveig for a boat. She said she would
not do them any favor without getting paid for it.

"There is an old boat in the boat shed, and I shall charge
you four ounces of silver for lending it."

Thorgils said that two ounces would be more than enough
for it. Kormák said he would not stand out for such a small

matter. Thorgils said he preferred to ride around the firth, but Kormák prevailed and they got aboard the boat. But they had got but a short way from land when the boat filled with water and they had trouble getting back to the spot they started from.

"You should have punishment rather than payment, you evil hag," Kormák said. Thórveig said she had not deceived them much. Then Kormák paid her the silver.

Kormák spoke this verse:

> 24a. Always am I, warrior,
>   at it—like a bat e'er
>   ready at spring[2]—to raise the
>   red-cheeked maid in skaldship.

> 24b. A pretty price, for sure, to
>   pay for this and that thing:
>   think now! Three whole ounces
>   Thórveig's boat will cost me.[3]

Bersi had quickly got him horses and rode home. Kormák saw he could not catch up with him and spoke this verse:

> 25. In such wise the winsome
>   woman—I had trusted
>   her before—passed from my
>   fathoming arms and kisses
>   that not e'er hereafter
>   I shall—yet I often
>   sated wolves on weapon-slain
>   warriors' bodies—have her.[4]

They mounted their horses and rounded the firth and met Váli. They asked about Bersi. Váli told them that Bersi had got to Múli and had gathered reinforcements: "They are very numerous."

"Then we have come too late," said Kormák, "seeing that they have gathered men."

Thorgils begged Kormák to turn back, because there was not much honor to be got now. Kormák replied that he wanted to see Steingerd. Váli went with them, and they arrived in Múli. There they found Bersi with a great number of men. They spoke to one another, and Kormák said Bersi had betrayed him in taking Steingerd away. "We now want to take the woman with us, and receive atonement for the dishonor done us."

Then Thórd Arndísarson said: "We are willing to come to an agreement with Kormák; but Bersi has power over the woman."

Bersi said: "There is no chance of Steingerd going with you; but I offer Kormák my sister in marriage, and I consider that he would be doing well if he is married to Helga."

Thorgils said: "This is an offer well worth considering, brother, and let us think about it." But Kormák would have none of it.

IX · KORMÁK BORROWS THE SWORD SKOFNUNG

THERE was a woman called Thórdís,[1] an evil-minded hag. She lived at Spákonu Fell (Wise-woman's Mountain) on the Skagastrand. She knew all about Kormák's affairs. She had come to Múli that day and now spoke up for him.

She said this: "Don't offer him a harlot; for this is a woman of low morals and not a fit mate for any respectable man, and his mother would not relish so poor a settlement for him."

Thórd said: "Get thee gone, thou evil hag!" and gave it as his opinion that Helga would prove herself to be a most excellent woman.

Kormák said: "This may all be true, (but) I don't care to accept this proposal."

Thorgils said: "It will bring us no luck to listen to the words of that fiend of a woman and not accept this proposal."

Then Kormák said: "I challenge you, Bersi, to go on the holm with me within half a month's time, on Leidholm[2] (Assembly Island) in Middale." It is now called Battle Island. Bersi said he would come. He said Kormák chose that which would bring him less honor.

Thereupon Kormák went to seek Steingerd at the farm, and reproached her for having betrayed him in taking another man as a husband.

Steingerd said: "It is you, Kormák, who failed me, to start with; yet all this was done without my consent."

Then Kormák spoke this verse:

> 26. I betrayed our tryst, you
> take it, Gefn-of-linen.[3]
> Still, to stay you, my good
> steed I winded wholly.
> Rather would I, ring-Eir,[3]
> ruin my best horse, though—
> hard I whipped the nag—than
> have you wed another.

Thereupon Kormák and his company returned home. Kormák told his mother how matters had turned out.

Dalla said: "Fortune will not smile upon you; because now you have refused an excellent match, and it looks hopeless for you to duel with Bersi. He is a powerful fighter and has good weapons." Bersi owned a sword called Hvíting, a mighty keen blade. With it went a healing-stone,[4] and with that sword he had fought in many a dangerous fight.

Dalla said: "What weapon will you have against Hvíting?"

Kormák said that he would use a large, keen battle-axe. Dalla thought it wise to look up Midfirth-Skeggi and ask him for the sword Skofnung.[5] Thereupon Kormák rode to Reykir and told Skeggi how matters stood and asked him to lend him Skofnung. Skeggi said that he was unwilling to do that. He declared that Kormák and the sword were of different tempers: "Skofnung is deliberate,[6] but you are impatient and rash."

Kormák rode away in an angry mood. He returned to Mel and told his mother that Skeggi did not want to lend him the sword. Skeggi had been giving Dalla advice in her affairs and they were good friends.

Dalla said: "He will lend you the sword, even though he may be slow to do so."

Kormák said it was not as it ought to be, "if he lets you have the sword but not me." Dalla said he had an ungovernable temper.

Several days later Dalla asked Kormák to go to Reykir. "Skeggi will let you have the sword now."

Kormák went to Skeggi and asked him for Skofnung.

"It may be difficult for you to manage it," said Skeggi. "A pouch goes with it, and you are not to touch that. The sun must not shine on the hilt above; and you are not to bare it except when ready to do battle. But so soon as you come to the place where the fight is to be, then sit down by yourself and draw it from the sheath. Point the blade forward and blow upon it. Then a little snake will creep forth from the hilt. Then lower the sword and make it easy for the snake to return into the hilt."

Kormák said: "Many are the tricks you have, you warlocks." Skeggi said: "And yet all will come about as I tell you."

Thereupon Kormák rode home and told his mother how matters had gone and wondered how much influence she had over Skeggi. He showed her the sword and wanted to draw it, but it would not leave the scabbard.

Dalla said: "You are too self-willed, my son." Thereupon Kormák set his foot on the hilt and tore off the pouch. Skofnung made a snarling noise at that and would not leave the scabbard.

Now the time for the duel approached. Kormák rode to it with fifteen men. Bersi likewise rode to the place of meeting with as many men. Kormák arrived first. Kormák said to Thorgils that he wanted to sit down by himself. He sat down and undid the sword, but was careless about not letting the sun shine upon the hilt. When he had girded himself with it outside his cloak and wanted to draw it, he could not do so without standing on the hilt. Then the little snake came out, but he did not proceed with it as he should have, and so its good luck had departed from the sword, and it came snarling out of its sheath.

X · THE HOLMGANG BETWEEN KORMÁK AND BERSI

THEREUPON Kormák rejoined his men. Bersi and his company had arrived by this time, and also a great number of other people, in order to watch this fight. Kormák took up Bersi's shield and struck it (with his sword), and fire flashed from it. Now a cloak was spread on the ground under their feet.

Bersi said: "You, Kormák, challenged me to the holm; but I propose single combat to you. You are a young man and little tried, and the holmgang is difficult, but the single combat, not at all."[1]

Kormák said: "I shall not put up a better fight in the single combat. I want to risk it and in every respect be your equal."

"Very well, then," said Bersi.

These were the rules for the holmgang: a cloak five ells square was to be laid down, with loops in the corners. Pegs with heads were to be rammed in there which were called tjǫsnur.[2] He who attended to this was to approach the tjǫsnur in such fashion that he looked up between his legs while holding on to his earlaps and speaking the spell which later was used in the so-called tjǫsnu sacrifice. Three borders (or furrows), each a foot in breadth, were to be around the cloak, and at the edge of these borders were to be four cords[3] which are called hǫslur (hazels). And when all this had been done then the spot was called "hazeled." Each contestant was to have three shields, and when they were destroyed then he was to step on the cloak again if he had left it before, and fend himself with his weapons thereafter. He who had been challenged was to have the first blow. If one of the two was

wounded so that blood flowed on the cloak, then no further
fighting was to be done. If either one stepped outside the
hǫslur with one foot, then that was called "he yields ground";
but "he flees," if with both. Each contestant was to have
someone to hold his shield before him. He who was wounded
hardest was to pay holm ransom—three marks of silver.

Thorgils held the shield for his brother, and Thórd Arndísarson, for Bersi. Bersi dealt the first blow and cleft Kormák's shield. And Kormák dealt Bersi a blow with the same
effect. Each shattered three shields of the other. Kormák had
the next blow and slashed at Bersi. The latter warded off the
blow with Hvíting, and Skofnung sheared off the point of
Hvíting in front of the hollow (running along the middle of
the blade). The point of the sword flew against Kormák's
hand so that he was wounded on his thumb. The joint of the
thumb was split, and blood flowed on to the cloak. Thereupon
men went between them to stop the fight.

Then Kormák said: "Small victory has Bersi got through
my mishap if we are separated now." But when Skofnung
had descended on Bersi's shield, a notch was made in the
sword and fire flashed from the shield which Thórveig had
given Bersi. Bersi now claimed the holmgang ransom. Kormák said it would be paid him; and so they parted.

XI · KORMÁK ENGAGES STEINAR'S HELP AND RETURNS SKOFNUNG

A MAN was called Steinar.[1] He was the son of Onund sjóni
and (thus) a brother of Kormák's mother Dalla. He dwelled
at Ellidi and was a great fighter. Kormák rode there from
the holm to find his kinsman Steinar, and told him how matters stood. Steinar was very much wrought up about it. Kormák said that he intended to leave the country, "but I expect
you to pay the fine to Bersi."

Steinar said: "I can't call you a man of great mettle; but

the money will be paid if necessary." Kormák stayed there several days. His hand swelled up greatly as it had not been bandaged.

After the holmgang, Bersi visited his brothers, and they asked him how the duel had turned out. He told them, and they thereupon said that two tough fighters had exchanged feeble blows there and that Bersi had won the victory only through Kormák's mishap. Bersi then came to Steingerd, and she asked how matters had turned out.

He spoke this verse:

> 27. Ounces three time eight the
> Ullr-of-sword-fray² had to
> pay me as the price of
> peace—a bold man call him!
> Will the Baldr-of-battle²—the
> best I had of it on
> isle—not ever after
> urge me on to holmgang.

Steinar and Kormák rode away from Ellidi and towards Saurbær.³ They saw a company of men riding in their direction, and it proved to be Bersi and his followers. He greeted Kormák and asked how his wound was. Kormák said that it required no more care.

Bersi said: "Would you like me to heal it⁴ though you have received it through me? And then it will soon be cured." Kormák refused that and said he would always bear him a grudge.

Then Bersi spoke this verse:

> 28. Hild's-storm⁵ recall, when to
> holm-fight thou hadst urged me!
> Gladly shall I go to
> game-of-swords—I am proven:
> Kormák's shield I cleft—the
> craven would no longer
> fight me on the fell⁶—in
> fray right down to the handle.

And with that they parted. Thereupon Kormák rode home
to Mel to his mother. She healed his hand. It became ugly
and healed with much proud flesh. The notch in Skofnung
they sought to mend by whetting it; but it grew the larger
the more it was whetted. Then Kormák rode over to Reykir
and cast Skofnung before Skeggi's feet and spoke this verse:

29. Sword edge-broken I bring you—
bit not the weapon, Skeggi!
Due to it, indeed, no
doubt they[7] came off better.
Take me not to task, nor
taunt me, either, that I,
warrior, failed in fighting
for that winsome maiden.

Skeggi said: "Things turned out as I thought they would."
Kormák rode away and home to Mel.

He spoke this verse:

30. In good stead 'twould stand me
stoutly to fight on holm, I
thought, 'gainst brave Bruin-of-
bosky-lair,[8] to win her.
But the wondrous wand-of-
wounds[9] broke in the fighting.
Luckless—I'm loathe to say—it
lost me a great treasure.[10]

And when he met his mother Dalla he spoke this verse:

31. Fickle proved and full of
flaws the sword of Skeggi.
Was the wand-of-wounds too
weak to use in combat.
Skofnung in the skirmish—
scars I made in Hvíting—
bit in twain the brittle
brand before the sword-hilt.

And again:

> 32. Was my wand-of-wounds found
> wanting when the fire-of-
> bucklers[11] to the battle I
> bore, for combat eager;
> grumbling sounds did give the
> grizzly-of-shields[12] as it
> unwilling out of den did
> issue, shields to splinter.

And still again:

> 33. Twice to tryst I wended,
> trinket-Gefn,[13] as pledged, on
> mornings twain, but missed the
> maid and so her favor.
> Gainless were't, I guess, to
> go from home to meet her—
> oft I sing the Ilm-of-
> armrings'[13] praise—a third time.[14]

Thereupon Kormák rode over to Reykir one day, and spoke with Skeggi. Skeggi said the holmgang had been fought in a paltry fashion.

Then Kormák spoke this verse:

> 34. Take me not to task if
> tardy I have been—my
> skaldship scout not!—bringing
> Skofnung to its owner;
> for that fate doth bend all
> Freys-of-helmets[15]—has the
> brand been borne in many a
> battle—under its power.

And again:

> 35. Hard I thrust, so thought I,
> thane, against my foeman's
> breast with the bloodthirsty
> blade which you did give me;

but the slaughterous sword, though
swung against her husband,
would not—I crave the woman—
wound him with its sharpness.

XII · BERSI FALLS OUT WITH THÓRD AND IS CHALLENGED BY STEINAR

IN THE winter there were games[1] at Saurbær. Both Ásmund, the son of Bersi, and the sons of Thórd Arndísarson
took part in them. The latter were younger and had less
strength than Ásmund. He did not control his strength so that
the sons of Thórd often came home black and blue and bloody.
Thórdís, their mother, was much put out by this and requested
Thórd to ask Bersi, Ásmund's father, to make amends to
him. Thórd was loath to do so.

Then she said: "In that case I shall go to see my brother
Bork, and that will not improve matters."[2]

Thórd begged her not to do that, "I would rather talk
with Bersi myself"; and according to her wishes he went to
Bersi and asked him to make amends.

Bersi said: "Now you are too greedy for money, and it
does not greatly redound to your honor to come with such
demands. But I shall not let you want so long as I have means
myself."[2a] Thórd rode home, and there was little friendship
between them that winter. Spring passed, and the time for the
Thórsness Assembly[3] was approaching. Bersi seemed to discern that it was Thórdís who had egged Thórd on to make
that claim on him.

Men now prepared to journey to the Assembly. It had been
the custom of Thórd and Bersi to make that journey together. Bersi left home and arrived in Múli, but Thórd had
left already.

Bersi said: "Now Thórd has broken our custom in not
waiting for me."

Then Thórdís answered: "It is you who caused the change; though that is slight retaliation, and more might come." It came to words between them, and Bersi said that ill would result from her advice. Then he rode away.

Bersi said (to his companions): "Let us proceed toward the firth and get us a boat; it is a long way around the firth."[4] They did get a boat there, which belonged to Thórd, and rode on till they came to the Assembly when most others had already arrived. They went to the booth of Ólaf Pá (Peacock) of Hjardarholt.[5] Bersi belonged to his district. There were many people in the booth, and Bersi found no seat.[6] He was accustomed to sit by the side of Thórd, but that seat was occupied. A man sat there, big and strongly made and clad in a bearskin cloak with a cowl over his face. Bersi stood before him, but the man made no move to get up for him. Bersi asked what his name was. He was told that he was called sometimes Glúm, sometimes Skúmi.[7]

Bersi spoke this verse:

36. Who in hide of bear hath
hither come to threaten?
But beware of wolfish
wills 'neath my sib's breast-bones.
Much this man does look to
me like Steinar, whether he—
to the holm we'll hie us[8]—
hight be Glúm or Skúmi.

"And you need not conceal your name, you man in the bearskin cloak," said Bersi.

"Right you are," said Steinar, "and I am to pay you a sum for Kormák, if that is necessary; but before I do so I challenge you to the holm. Maybe then you will get three marks or else lose both."

Then Bersi spoke this verse:

37. Asked I am, ye gale-of-
arrows-urgers[9] skilled in
war—nor wince I thereat—
with you to go on holm now.

> Old I am, but trained in
> iron-handed war, nor—
> feeders-fierce-of-wolf-brood[10]—
> flinch I e'er in sword-play.[11]

"And it is clear that you kinsmen wish to destroy me. It is well, too, that you should find out whether it is better to have me as a friend or as an enemy and that your overbearing is taken down a peg."

Steinar said: "We are not after your life, but we would like you to come down off your high horse."

Bersi accepted the challenge and went into a separate booth and stayed there (during the Assembly).

One day it was announced that there would be a swimming contest.

Steinar said to Bersi: "Would you care to match yourself in swimming with me, Bersi?"

He replied: "I have not been swimming lately, yet I shall try it."

Bersi swam swiftly and strongly. He wore an amulet (healing-stone) about his neck. Steinar swam up to him and snatched it away from him, together with the pouch in which it was kept, and threw it into the water.

He spoke this verse:

> 38.[12] Long have I lived
> and let the gods rule:
> never had I
> hose mossbrown dyed;[13]
> never bound I
> a bag to my neck
> stuffed with simples,
> and still I live.

Then they both swam to land. The trick Steinar played on Bersi was due to the advice of Thórd in order that Bersi should have the worst of it in the holmgang. Thórd went along the firth at ebb tide. He found the amulet and guarded it. Steinar had the sword which was called Skrýmir.[14] It never became rusty, nor was it difficult to manage.

On the day agreed on for the holmgang Thórd and Steinar left their booth, and Kormák went to the assembly. Ólaf Pá gave Bersi men to accompany him to the holm. Thórd Arndísarson had been accustomed to hold the shield for Bersi, but that he did no longer. Yet Bersi went on the holm, but his shield bearer is not mentioned by name. Kormák was to hold the shield for Steinar. Bersi had the shield which Thórveig had given him. Each contestant had three shields. Bersi shattered two of Steinar's shields, and Kormák was holding the third for him. Bersi hewed again at Steinar, but his sword Hvíting stuck in the iron rim of Steinar's shield. Kormák then jerked up the shield, and in that moment Steinar hewed at Bersi. The blow fell on Bersi's shield, and from its edge glanced off on Bersi's buttocks and from there along the thigh into the hollow of the leg where it fastened in the bone, so that Bersi fell.

Then Steinar said: "Now the fee is paid for Kormák."

Bersi leaped up then and struck at Steinar, cleaving his shield, and the point of his sword pierced Steinar's breast. Thórd quickly pulled Steinar away.

Thórd said: "Now I repaid you for the manhandling of my sons."

Thereupon Bersi was borne to his booth and his wounds bandaged. Thórd came into his booth, and when Bersi saw him he spoke this verse:

> 39. Formerly you followed,
> Frey-of-combats,[15] me when
> in my hand the eager
> axe bit into shield-rims:
> truly yet the targes-
> trusty-maiden[16] helps me—
> thou'rt, Frey-of-helmets,[17] fickle and
> false grown—in the sword-fray.[18]

And then this one:

> 40. Held men that for Hlokk's-gale[19]
> wholly fit I was, when
> younger—of yore 'twas said—and
> yea, did stand my ground well.

> Now my own kin—naught I
> need to hide it—think I'm—
> Saurbær's flat fields did that[20]—
> fit for burial only.

Thórd said: "We did not wish you dead, this time, but we are glad to see you humbled."

Then Bersi spoke this verse:

> 41. Lo! now in the lurch have
> left me—'t must be said, though,
> hopes of happiness I
> have none—my own kinsmen.
> Faithful friends—I often
> fed the greedy ravens—
> nowise am I awed by
> oaths[21]—are hard to come by.

Then Bersi was brought home to Saurbær and was a long time recovering from his wounds.

There remains to tell about Kormák and Steinar. At that time when Bersi was borne to his booth, Steinar spoke this verse before Kormák:

> 42. Four and eight of foemen
> felled I—you have heard of
> that—in skirmish, skald, with
> Skrymir's polished sword-blade.
> Now, at the last, low was
> laid by him who pours the
> beer-of-Bestla's-kinsman,[22]
> Bersi, with flashing blood-wand.

Steinar said: "I want you now to have Skrýmir, Kormák; because I think this has been my last holmgang."

Thereupon they parted as friends. Steinar rode to his home, and Kormák, to Mel.

XIII · STEINGERD DIVORCES BERSI

Now it is related about Bersi that his wounds healed with difficulty. One time when many people were visiting him, the talk fell on the fight and how it had turned out. Then Bersi spoke this verse:

> 43. Ygg-of-gold,[1] you under
> edge did hold me, whilst you—
> need compels me now to
> name it—sheltered Steinar.
> Let be!—lesser things be-
> like have stirred my wrath oft.
> That will, Thórd, now over-
> throw our former friendship.[2]

Thereupon Thórd went to the bed where Bersi lay and gave him the healing-stone. Then Thórd cured Bersi and they became friends as before and remained so.

In consequence of these events Steingerd took a deep dislike to Bersi and wished to divorce him;[3] and when she was about to leave him she went up to him and said: "First you were called Eyglu-Bersi, and then, Holmgang-Bersi; but now you might in truth be called Buttocks-Bersi," and declared her divorce from him. Steingerd rode north[4] to her kinsfolk. She met her brother Thorkel and requested him to fetch her property from Bersi, both morning-gift[5] and dowry. She said she did not want to be married to that cripple, Bersi. Thorkel did not reproach her and promised to attend to the matter. The winter wore on and Thorkel's errand was put off.

XIV · BERSI SLAYS THORKEL

LATER, in the spring Thorkel Toothgnasher rode away to look up Holmgang-Bersi and take along with him Steingerd's possessions. Bersi said that his lot was heavy enough, even though both parties bore their share of trouble[1]—"and I am not going to hand over the property."

Thorkel said: "I challenge you to the holmgang on Or-rostuholm (Battle-Isle) by Tialdanes (Tent-Ness)."[2]

Bersi said: "That may seem a small thing to such a champion as you are; yet I promise you to come."

Both appeared at the holm, and the fight began. Thórd Arndísarson held the shield for Bersi, and Váli, for Thorkel. And when two shields (of each contestant) had been shattered, Bersi requested Thorkel to take up the third. Thorkel refused to do that. Bersi (still) had a shield and a long, and keen sword.

Thorkel said: "The sword you have there, Bersi, is longer than is allowed under the rules."

"That shall not be," said Bersi; and seizing (his other sword) Hvíting with both hands he dealt Thorkel the death-blow.

Then Bersi spoke this verse:

> 44. Now Toothgnasher too—my
> teeth I showed[2a]—I slaughtered—
> would that men widely spread my
> words!—as thirty-first one:
> all the more, though old, the
> Ullr-of-ships[3]—I fed oft
> wolves—shall welcome be in
> world to come, with Odin.[4]

Thereupon Váli challenged Bersi to the holm, but Bersi spoke this verse:

> 45.[5] Bidden am I, byrnie-
> bearers masterful in
> war—nor wince I thereat—
> with you to try the holmgang:
> gamesome seems it to gallants—
> grim sword-play I shun not
> e'er—to dare me to deadly
> duel on the island.

As they were about to begin to fight, Thórd went between them and said to Bersi and Váli: "It would seem a great shame for valiant men (like you) to fell each other without sufficient reason, and I offer to arbitrate between you."

Both agreed to that.

Thórd said: "It seems to me, Váli, that the likeliest way to reach an agreement would be for you to let Bersi have your sister Thórdís in marriage. That would be an honor to you."

Bersi agreed to this, and Thórdís was to take the farm Brekkuland[6] along as her dowry. So this marriage agreement was made between them. Afterwards Bersi had defences prepared around his farm and dwelled there many years in peace.

XV · BERSI RESCUES STEINVOR AND KILLS THÓRARIN AND HIS SONS

A CERTAIN MAN was called Thórarin.[1] He was the son of Álf and lived to the north in Thambárdale, which opens up on the Bitrufirth. He was a big and powerfully built man and therefore called Thórarin the Strong. He had been on long journeys abroad and was so fortunate in them that he always ran into the harbors which he intended to make. He had three sons—one called Álf, another, Lopt, and the third, Skopti. Thórarin was a most overbearing man, and his sons took after him and were boisterous and self-assertive fellows. Another man was called Odd. He dwelt at Tunga, which lies by the Bitrufirth. He had a daughter called Steinvor, a handsome and well-made woman. She was known by the name of Mjóbeina (Slender-Ankle). Together with Odd there lived many fishermen. At the fishing station there was a man called Glúm, an ill-tempered, repulsive fellow.

One time Odd and Glúm talked about who were the foremost men in the district. Glúm considered Thórarin the greatest, but Odd said that Holmgang-Bersi was in every respect his superior.

Glúm said: "What proof have you for that?"

Odd replied: "Can there be any comparison between Bersi's manhood and Thórarin's thefts?"

And the two continued arguing about this till they lost their tempers and wagered about it. Then Glúm went and told Thórarin. Thórarin became very angry and cursed Odd. Thereupon Thórarin seized Steinvor and took her to Tunga without the permission of her father Odd. He said to Odd that if he complained about it it would be at his own peril. Thórarin and Steinvor arrived in Thambárdale, and nothing happened for a while.

Thereupon Odd went to Holmgang-Bersi and told him how matters had gone and asked him for help to fetch back Steinvor and avenge the insult done him. Bersi said that the dispute had been an idle one and told Odd to go home and do nothing about it—"and yet I promise you my help."

As soon as Odd was gone Bersi made himself ready to leave. He rode all armed, girded with the sword Hvíting and carrying three spears in his hand. He arrived in Thambárdale toward dusk as the women were leaving their quarters. Steinvor caught sight of Bersi and went out to greet him and told him her misfortune. "Make ready to go with me," said Bersi, and she did so.

Bersi said that he had not intended to come to Thambárdale for nothing, and went up to the door (of the hall) where the men were sitting by the long-fires.[2] He knocked at the door, and a man came out who called himself Thorleif. Thórarin recognized Bersi's voice and ran out with a big carving knife and thrust at Bersi. Bersi saw him coming. He drew Hvíting and dealt him a death-blow at once. Then Bersi leaped on his horse. He put Steinvor on the horse before him and took from her the spears which she had kept for him. He rode to the woods and there hid the horse and Steinvor, asking her to wait for him there. Then he went to the rock defile[3] through which the common road led and there prepared (to meet those who would pursue him).

In Thambárdale there was much confusion. Thorleif ran and told the sons of Thórarin that he lay slain in the doorway. They asked who had done the deed, and he told them. Thereupon they set out to find Bersi and made directly for the rocks, intending to head him off; but he was there before them. And when they approached, Bersi hurled a spear at Álf and it went through him. Thereupon Lopt threw his spear at Bersi. He caught it on his shield and it glanced off. Then Bersi hurled a spear at Lopt and killed him, and then also Skopti. When all this had happened the servants of the brothers came up. Thorleif turned back to them and they all retired to the farm.

XVI · BERSI KILLS VÁLI

THEREUPON Bersi went back to Steinvor and mounted his horse (with her) and arrived at home (in the morning) before people had gotten up. They asked him where he had been and he told them. And when Thórd met Bersi he asked how matters had gone in their fight.

Then Bersi spoke this verse:

> 46. Fell one feeder-of-wolves[1] the
> first in Thambárdale, when
> Thórarin I thrust right
> through (before his threshold).
> Lost their lives also, with
> Lopt, they Álf and Skopti:
> father and sons, the four, were
> fey. Alone I slew them.

Thereupon Odd returned to his home, but Steinvor remained with Bersi. This greatly displeased Thórdís. At that time Bersi's fortification had become somewhat dilapidated, but now he had it put into good condition. We are told that no atonement was made for the death of these men. Now some time passed.

One day when Thórdís and Bersi were talking together he said: "I have thought of offering Ólaf Hoskuldsson to take his child in fosterage."[2]

She replied: "That is not to my liking. It would seem to me a difficult undertaking and one not likely to bring us much honor."

"It is a connection to be relied on; I have many enemies and have begun to age considerably," said Bersi. He went to visit Ólaf and offered to foster one of his children. Ólaf accepted this with thanks, and Bersi took Halldór home with him and had Steinvor bring him up. This displeased Thórdís and she begrudged them every penny. Now Bersi began to age considerably.

One time the men under him in the district came to visit Bersi. He sat by himself and received his food before the others did. Bersi had porridge while the other men ate cheese and curds.

Then Bersi spoke this verse:

> 47. Sooty-feathered fowls-of-
> frays[3] with bodies of my
> fallen foes I've sated
> five and thirty times now:
> trolls my life may take if
> trusty sword with blood I'll
> redden no more: then may the
> men put me away fast.

Halldór said: "You are still minded to kill someone, foster-father mine."

Bersi said: "I know one who deserves it."

Thórdís allowed her brother the use of the pasturage at Brekkuland. Bersi had his servants stay close to the farm and have nothing to do with Váli. Halldór did not like it that Bersi could not dispose of his own property.

Thereupon Bersi spoke this verse:

> 48.[4] We both do lie
> on bench[5] together,
> Halldór and I,
> quite helpless both:
> does youth for thee
> but age for me:
> 'twill mend with thee,
> no more with me.

Halldór said: "I much dislike Váli."
Bersi spoke this verse:

> 49. Fleering, Váli feeds his
> flock on our own pastures:
> well I know the warrior
> walks right boldly o'er us.
> Lesser taunts have tried my
> temper oft—for which the
> wand-of-wounds[6] I reddened
> with the blood of foemen.

And again:

> 50. Age has all unstrung the
> Ullr-of-golden-armrings:[7]
> much I must abide from
> men without redress now.
> Still, although they threaten to
> thrust me in my cold grave,
> fearless first with sword I'll
> fight, nor let them awe me.

Halldór said: "Stout is your heart as yet, foster-father mine."

Steinvor and Bersi had a talk together. Bersi said to her: "I have a plan in mind, and I need you for it." She said she owed it to him to do all she could for him. "You are to get into a fuss with Thórdís about a milk pail and hold on to it until you spill the milk. At that point I shall come in and take her side. Then you[8] shall go to Váli and tell him how you have been ill treated."

Things went as Bersi had planned, and she came to Váli and told him how badly she had been treated. She requested him to accompany her to the rocky defile[9] (on her way home to her father), and he did so. As Váli was about to turn back, Bersi and Halldór met him. Bersi had a halberd in one hand and a staff in the other, and Halldór was armed with the sword Hvíting. As soon as Váli saw them he went to the attack and leveled a blow at Bersi. Halldór got behind Váli and tried to hamstring him with Hvíting. Then Váli turned about quickly to fight Halldór. In that moment Bersi pierced him between the shoulderblades with his halberd. That was his death-wound. Then they set up his shield at his feet and his sword at his head and covered him with his cloak, and then they mounted their horses and rode to five farms to announce the slaying and who had done the deed,[10] and then they rode home. People went to take care of the remains of Váli; and the place where he was killed is called Válafell since that time. Halldór had come to be twelve years old when this took place.

XVII · STEINGERD MARRIES THORVALD

A CERTAIN MAN was called Thorvald. He was the son of Eystein and had the nickname of Tintein.[1] He was wealthy and clever with his hands, a skald, but not notable for great spirit. His brother was called Thorvard and lived in the north at Fliót. They had a great many kinsmen, and the clan was called the Skídings. They did not enjoy much popularity.[1a]

Thorvald Tintein asked Steingerd in marriage, and with the consent of her kinsfolk she was given to him, nor was she averse to it. That was the same summer that Steingerd had left Bersi. Kormák heard of this but acted as though he knew nothing of it. Shortly before, Kormák had transported his wares to his ship and intended to go abroad—he and his brother. Early one morning Kormák left the ship and rode to visit Steingerd.[2] He talked with her and asked her to make him a shirt.[3] She said his coming was uncalled for and that Thorvald and his kinsmen would not stand for it without avenging themselves. Kormák spoke this verse:

51. I can't understand at
    all why you should have been,
    guardian-of-the-gold-lace,
    given to that tinsmith.

Silken-Nanna,[4] seldom
smile I since that, glorious
woman, to this weakling
wedded thee thy father.

Steingerd said: "Your words make your hatred only too
clear, and I shall tell Thorvald about your insults—no man
would put up with such an affront." Then Kormák spoke
this verse:

> 52. Need is none to threaten,
> Nanna-of-the-wimple,[4]—
> well I can beware me—
> with the Skídings' hatred:
> twit and taunt I shall his
> tribe the very stones shall—
> fey I ween the fellows—
> float upon the water.

Thereupon they parted in great bitterness, and Kormák
returned to his ship.

XVIII · KORMÁK AND THORGILS IN VIKING RAIDS ABROAD

WHEN the brothers left the moorings, a walrus broke
water close by their ship. Kormák hurled a heavy spear at it.
He hit the animal and it disappeared in the water. Men
thought it had the eyes of Thórveig.[1] This walrus did not
come up afterwards; but of Thórveig it was told that she lay
mortally ill, and people say that she died from that illness.

Then they made for the open sea and arrived in Norway.
At that time Hákon, the foster-son of King Æthelstan, ruled
Norway.[2] The two brothers went at once to pay their respects
to the king, and he received them well. They remained at his
court that winter in great honor. The summer after they went

on a viking expedition and accomplished great deeds. A man called Sigurd, a German of noble extraction, was their companion. They raided in many parts. One day when they had gone up on land eleven men attacked the brothers. The outcome of the fray was that the brothers overcame all eleven. Then they returned to their ship. Their crew had given them up for lost and welcomed them with joy when they returned with the victory and booty. On this expedition the brothers won great fame.

The summer wore on and winter approached. Then they wished to steer their course to Norway. They struck cold weather, and the sail was coated with hoarfrost. The two brothers were always in the forefront. On that occasion Kormák spoke this verse:

> 53. Shake we—shivery is the
>   shack I have—the snow—with
>   hoarfrost hooded are the
>   high fells—from the tent roof.[3]
>   Would the lazy weakling
>   were as coldly bedded—
>   the boor ne'er budges from his
>   buxom white-armed leman.

Thorgils said: "You are always talking about her now, but when you had the chance you did not want her."

Kormák replied: "More was this the work of ill wights than due to my own waywardness."[4] Presently they sailed close to some cliffs and had to lower the sails in great danger.

Kormák said: "Would that Thorvald Tintein were here with us!"

Thorgils smiled and said: "More likely that he has an easier time today than we."

"Then it is not as it ought to be," replied Kormák. Shortly thereafter they made Norway.

XIX · KORMÁK FIGHTS IN KING HAROLD'S EXPEDITIONS. KORMÁK RETURNS TO ICELAND AND ENCOUNTERS STEINGERD

WHILE they had been gone a change of rulers had taken place in Norway. Hákon had died, and Harold Grayfur[1] had taken his place. They tendered their friendship to the king, and he accepted it. They sailed to Ireland with the king and fought battles there. One time when they had gone up on land with the king a great host came against them, and when the two armies were about to join battle Kormák spoke this verse:

> 54. I shun not death, though shield 'gainst
> shield will clash; nor will our
> noble king e'er need to
> nag me to the onset,
> Skarthi,[2] whilst the skald his
> skerries'-land-tree,[3] Thorkel's
> shapely daughter—shipmate,
> sharp that sorrow!—longs for.

Thorgils said: "There is not the time when you are in danger but your mind reverts to Steingerd."

Kormák said: "She is always in my mind still."

It was a big battle. King Harold won the victory, and his men pursued the fleeing host. The two brothers were stationed together when nine men attacked them, and they fought together for a while.

Kormák spoke this verse:

> 55. Straight shall we, Skarthi, stoutly
> striving 'gainst the enemy,
> the life take—lo! we two a-
> lone, brother—of nine men,
> whilst the slender silken-
> Sif,[4] she who does love me,
> goes to her god-detested
> gaffer's bed in Iceland.

Thorgils said: "Again you come to speak of the same matter."

The skirmish ended with the two brothers gaining the upper hand and slaying the nine men. For this they were praised highly by the king and shown much honor. The two brothers always accompanied the king on his expeditions. Then Thorgils observed that Kormák was sleeping very little all the time and asked him the reason. Then Kormák spoke this verse:

> 56. Steep slopes-of-the-stormy-
>   strands-of-Haki's-blue-land[5]
>   roar, and rear up, but to
>   rush back, foaming, sea-ward.
>   Sleepless, say you, o'er the
>   silver-dight one am I,
>   more than you: the maid I
>   miss whenever I waken.

"And I herewith serve notice to you, brother, that I intend to sail back to Iceland."

Thorgils said: "Many are the obstacles you will meet there, and I cannot foretell what the outcome will be."

As soon as the king heard of Kormák's intention to leave him he summoned him and said he was acting unwisely and tried to dissuade him from making that journey, but to no avail. Kormák took ship. When they put out to sea they struck stormy weather. The waves broke over the ship, and their sailyard snapped.

Then Kormák spoke this verse:

> 57. Other far this fix than
>   faces Tintein when his
>   drudge—the cur would dread this
>   danger—breaks a muck sled:
>   now in Solund Sound[6] the
>   sailyard of the sea-steed[7]—
>   are all weapon-wielders[8]
>   witness—is all mended.

They made the high sea and had stormy weather. One time when a great wave swept over the ship and the men were wet Kormák spoke this verse:

> 58.   Little knows the nerveless
>   gnawer-of-tin[9] who shuns the
>   raging sea—e'er robs my
>   rest the Ilm-of-jewels[10]—
>   how the fiery flood[11] oft
>   falls upon the sailor:
>   he can hie him to his
>   haven in wife's embraces.

They had a stormy passage but at last made land in the Midfirth and cast anchor not far from shore. They saw a woman riding up on land. Kormák recognized Steingerd and had the boat lowered and rowed to land. He left the boat quickly and got himself a horse and rode to meet Steingerd.[12] And when they met, Kormák leaped from horseback and lifted her out of the saddle and set her down beside him. The horses strayed away from them. The day drew to an end and darkness was coming on.

Steingerd said: "It is time to look for our horses."

He said it would be an easy matter (to find them). He looked about and did not see the horses anywhere, but they had straggled in the bed of a creek not far from where both had been sitting. Now night came on, so they took to walking and came to a small farm. They were taken in there and given such hospitality as they needed. During the night, each lay on his side of a wooden partition. Then Kormák spoke this verse:

> 59.   Side by side we rest here,
>   Sif-of-jewels,[13]—I fear we're
>   prey to hostile powers—
>   parted by a wall, though:
>   when, oh when, I wonder,
>   (Hild-of-silken-ribbons)[13]
>   shall we, free from fretting,
>   (fair one) sleep together?

Steingerd said it was better that they should not meet again. Kormák spoke this verse:

> 60. Five nights frightful did we,
> Freya-of-golden-trinkets,[14]
> in the same house sadly
> sleep, but not together;
> nightly lay I longing,
> linen-Sif,[14] in bedstead—
> all but empty-headed
> else—for thy embraces.[15]

Steingerd said: "All that is past and gone, so don't mention it again." Kormák spoke this verse:

> 61. Rugged rocks like grain will
> rather float, the land sink—
> unwelcome to the winsome
> woman am I ever—
> and the famous fells will
> fall into the ocean,
> born to the world ere will be
> woman as fair as Steingerd.[16]

Steingerd said she cared not to have him mock her. Kormák spoke this verse:

> 62. Oft and oft comes to me
> in my sleep the vision—
> but my fancy fools me—
> fairest Gefn-of-jewels,[17]
> by and by, thou Frigg-of-
> bracelets,[17] that thy arms did
> wind (all like a wedded
> wife's) about my body.

Steingerd said: "That is not going to happen if I can help it—you broke off all our engagements in such fashion that now you had better give up all hope."

Then they passed the night in sleep. In the morning when Kormák made ready to leave he went to see Steingerd and pulled a ring from his finger to give it to her.

She said: "The devil take you and your gold."
Then Kormák spoke this verse:

> 63. On ill-omened day I
> offered, 'gainst her kerchief—
> good days none were given[18]—my
> gold-ring to the maiden;
> but with blithesome mind[19] she
> bade me—neither would the
> maid have me or aught of
> mine—go to the devil.

He rode away in a dudgeon with Steingerd, but still more
with Tintein. He rode to his home at Mel and stayed there
during the winter but found winter quarters for the merchants who had come with him near the ship.

XX · KORMÁK IS SLANDERED

THORVALD TINTEIN lived north in Svínadale, and his
brother Thorvard, in Flíot. One day in winter Kormák journeyed north[1] to Svínadale in order to visit Steingerd. There he
dismounted and went to the living room. Steingerd was sitting on the dais, and Kormák seated himself by her; but
Thorvald sat on the bench with Narfi beside him.

Narfi said to Thorvald: "Are you not going to have anything to say about where Kormák is to sit? Are you going to
put up with this?"

Thorvald said: "I see nothing amiss about that. It is no
dishonor to me though they talk together."

Narfi said: "So much the worse for you."

Shortly afterwards the two brothers met, and Thorvald
told Thorvard about Kormák's coming there.

Thorvard said: "And do you stand for that?" Thorvald
said that he had not objected so far but that Kormák's visits
irked him.

Then Thorvard said: "I shall think of a way to prevent

them, if you don't dare to, because it is a disgrace to us all."

The next thing that happened was that when Thorvard (again) came to Svínadale the two brothers and Narfi bribed a vagabond to recite a verse in Steingerd's hearing and say that Kormák had composed it, though that was not the case. They said (also) that Kormák had taught it to a woman called Eylaug, a kinswoman of his. But this was the verse:

> 64. Would I that the woman
> were a jade in heat, and
> I a stallion in stud with
> Steingerd—(we together):
> would I then on Thrúd-of-
> threads² her back—* * *
> * * *³ have leapt right quickly.

Steingerd was so furious about it that she refused even to hear Kormák's name mentioned.

Kormák learned about this and went to visit Steingerd. For a long time he tried to get to speak with her, and in the end she answered and told him that she resented his making lampoons about her—"and it is known now over all the district." Kormák said there was no truth in that.

Steingerd said: "You might easily deny it if I had not heard it myself."

Kormák said: "Who spoke it in your presence?"

She told him who had recited the verse—"and you don't need to expect ever again to speak with me if this proves to be true."

Kormák rode off to look for the vagabond and found him and made him confess the truth. Kormák was beside himself with rage and fell upon Narfi and slew him. He meant to deal likewise with Thorvald, but he hid himself in shame, and some men stepped in between them and kept them apart. Then Kormák spoke this verse:

> 65. (Except for the first two lines,
> which are unintelligible, the
> stanza is the same as 52.)

All this got about in the district, and the hostility between them only increased. The brothers Thorvald and Thorvard were boastful about the affair, but it galled Kormák greatly.

XXI · THORVARD CHALLENGES KORMÁK BUT FAILS TO COME TO THE SINGLE COMBAT

THEREUPON Thorvard sent word to Kormák from Fliót that he challenged him to fight on the holm. He named the place and the time and said that he wanted to avenge himself now for Kormák's lampooning verses and other insults. Kormák accepted the challenge; and when the day agreed upon approached he went to the place designated. But neither Thorvard nor any one of his men showed up. Kormák encountered a woman on a farm (nearby). She greeted him and they asked each other the news.

She said: "What is your errand here, and for whom are you waiting?" Kormák spoke this verse:

> 66. Slow to come to sword-fight
> seems to me the dauntless
> feeder-of-wolves[1] from Fleetdale,
> from the north who challenged:
> should the hero have a
> heart of mud[2]—albeit the
> woman's husband[3] wants it
> worse even—made for him!

Kormák said: "Now I challenge Thorvard anew to the holm if he has the courage to come. Let him be called a common coward before all if he does not come"; and thereupon he spoke a verse:

> 67. Scarcely will the scoundrels
> 'scape—forsooth good cause they
> have for hate—Gaut's-gift[4] up-
> hold I e'er—my verses.[5]

Will the warriors find, I
warn them now—unless the
cowards cut me down by
cunning—that I yield not.[6]

Then the brothers Thorvald and Thorvard entered suit
against Kormák for defamation. Kormák's kinsmen came
to his defence, but he refused to make any reparation but said
that they deserved to be shamed rather than to be honored
and that he was all prepared for them unless they meant to
trick him. Thorvard had not shown up at the place agreed
upon for the fight to which Kormák had challenged him.
Kormák said that they had incurred the disgrace through
their own fault and that they therefore deserved to suffer the
consequences.

The time for the Húnavatn Assembly[7] approached, and
both parties attended it. One time when they met, Thorvard
and Kormák, Thorvard said: "For many affronts and insults
we have to repay you, and because of that I challenge you to
the holm here at the assembly."

Kormák said: "I wonder if you will do better than before,
for you have always dodged the fight."

"We shall try conclusions, for all that," said Thorvard;
"we shall no longer stand such affronts." Kormák said that
he would not keep him waiting, and returned to Mel.

XXII · KORMÁK'S VISIT TO THE SORCERESS THÓRDÍS. HE LAMES THORVARD

A MAN CALLED THÓRÓLF lived on the slopes of Spákonu
Fell. He was married to the witch Thórdís whom we have
mentioned before. Both attended the assembly, and many had
confidence in her help. Thorvard sought her out and asked
for assistance against Kormák. He gave her money for that,
and Thórdís made him ready for the duel as she thought best.

Kormák told his mother what he planned to do. She asked him whether he expected to be successful.

"Why shouldn't I?" replied Kormák.

Dalla said: "It will not do for you (to try the holmgang without preparation); because Thorvard is hardly likely to fight unless with the aid of witchcraft. My advice would be that you go to Thórdís the wise-woman, for there is likely to be trickery."

Kormák said: "I don't very much like to"; nevertheless he went to Thórdís and asked her to help him.

She said: "You come too late, for no weapons will wound him now. Yet I shall not refuse to help you. Stay here to-night, perhaps you will be lucky and I may see to it that iron will not harm you, either."

Kormák remained there over night. He awoke with some-one groping under the bedclothes at his head. He asked who was there, but the person turned to go and left by the outer door. Kormák went after her, and saw that it was Thórdís; and by that time she had got to the spot where the combat was to take place and had a goose under her arm. Kormák asked what was the meaning of all that.

She put the tame goose down and said: "Why couldn't you remain quiet?" Then Kormák lay down again but kept watch because he wanted to find out what her doings would be. She came three times, and every time he tried to find out what she was about. The third time Kormák went outside she had slaughtered two geese and let their blood run into a bowl.[1] She was about to slaughter the third when Kormák asked: "What are all these doings for, little mother?"

Thórdís said: "You are certainly a hard person to help, Kormák. I had wanted to overcome the evil fate which Thór-veig has called down on you and Steingerd; and you two could have enjoyed each other's love if I had been able to slaughter the third goose without anyone's seeing it."

Kormák said: "I don't believe in that kind of thing," and spoke a verse:

68. Ounces gave I on island
each time—twice the beldam
bled the birds—so that the
better I'd get of Thorvard:
blood there'll flow from blood—let
be to offer such to
skald the matchless mead² who
masters—of two ganders!³

They went on the holm. Thorvard had given the wise-
woman more money, and it was he who received (the benefit
of) the sacrifice. Kormák spoke this verse:

69. Much the trolls have trodden⁴—
trust no man another's
wife⁵—this woman: she's surely
wicked, to aid Thorvard.
Wonder were it nowise,
now weapon-thing⁶ begins, if
dire woe be due—what
doubt?—to the hoarse old sorceress.

Thórdís said: "I can manage it so that you will not feel the
blows."

Kormák gave her an ugly answer and said that she was
only doing mischief and wanted to drag her out of doors to
look at her eyes in the sunlight.⁷ Thorgils prevented him from
doing that and said no good would come of it.

Steingerd said she wanted to come to the holm, and so she
did. When Kormák saw her he spoke this verse:

70. Have I gone on holm now
Hlín-of-golden-rings⁸—what
stress could stop my love for
Steingerd?—twice for thy sake;
twice eke, silken-Sif, my
sword I reddened for thee.
Closer, therefore, thou shouldst
think me than that Tintein.

Then they fought. Kormák's sword would not cut. They had a long exchange of blows, and the sword of neither one cut. At last Kormák leveled a blow at Thorvard's side. It was a mighty stroke so that he reeled and his ribs cracked. He was knocked out, and so they parted. Kormák saw an ox standing (nearby) and slew it.[9] He had grown warm, so he took off his helmet and spoke this verse:

> 71. Have I gone on holm, thou
> Hlín-of-jewels,[10] for combat—
> nor shalt, linen-dight lady,
> let my going a third time.
> Red blood reddens not the
> reed-of-battle[11] this time,
> since the sorceress my
> sword's edge dulled by witchcraft.

He dried off his sweat on the corner of Steingerd's mantle.[12] Kormák spoke this verse:

> 72. Oft, since obdurate I
> am, my sweat I'll dry—much
> hardship had I through the
> Hlín-of-gold[13]—on mantle.
> Therefore let the thrall now—
> though of death more worthy—
> sniveling to his settle
> slink;—you caused me sorrow.[14]

Kormák asked Steingerd to go along with him, but she said she would choose herself with whom she would go. They parted, and both were much put out about it.

Thorvard was carried to his home, and Steingerd bandaged his injuries. Now Kormák kept on visiting Steingerd. Thorvard recovered only slowly; but as soon as he could move he went to look up Thórdís and asked her what he should do to recover.

She said: "Not far from here is a hillock in which the elves live. Get the bull that was slaughtered by Kormák and redden

the hillock with his blood and make a sacrifice of his meat to
the elves, and then you will get better."

Thereupon they sent word to Kormák that they wished to
buy the ox. He said he was willing to sell him, but only for
the ring which Steingerd had. They went to fetch the bull and
gave Kormák the ring and then did with the bull as Thórdís
had told them. Kormák spoke this verse:

> 73. This, the lady linen-dight will
> likely ask you warriors
> both, as red from bullock's
> bloodshed you return now:
> "Where's my red gold ring? You
> wrought much ill, unwisely"
> You sold it Ogmund's son, the
> swart-skinned, famed for skaldship.

It turned out as Kormák had surmised: Steingerd was
angry that they had made away with her ring.

XXIII · THORVARD DUELS WITH KORMÁK AGAIN AND IS INCAPACITATED

THEREAFTER Thorvard regained his health quickly. When
he thought he had regained his strength, he rode to Mel and
challenged Kormák to the holm.

Kormák said: "You have not had enough punishment yet,
but I shall accept."

So they both went to the holm. Thórdís came to visit Thorvard as she had done before. But Kormák did not seek her
help. She blunted his sword so it did not cut, yet he gave
Thorvard such a mighty blow on his shoulder that his shoul-
derblade broke and his arm immediately became useless and
he had to pay another ring as release from the holm. Then

Thórólf from Spákonu Fell ran up and dealt Kormák a blow.
He warded it off and spoke this verse:

74. Wrothly the reddener-of-
rusty-sword[1] assailed me—
Fiolnir's[2]-mead I fashion—;
faugh on the low-born scoundrel!
Nor was in that onrush
aught of damage done me—
feckless folly was it—
from the witch's husband.

Kormák slaughtered the sacrificial bull, as was the custom,
and said: "We are ill stead if we are to pocket both your attack and the witchcraft of Thórdís," and spoke this verse:

75. Dulled my wand-of-wounds the
witch—I had to let my
shield-hound[3] shatter Thorvard's
shoulder—at the holmgang:
blunt, it bit not well when
bent I was to strike him.
Still, so strong the blow I
struck he'll not forget it.

Thereupon both journeyed home, neither being satisfied
with the outcome.

XXIV · KORMÁK AS WELL AS STEINGERD AND THORVALD SAIL TO NORWAY

THE SHIP of the two brothers, Kormák and Thorgils, was
laid up ashore in the Hrútafirth during the winter. Toward
spring the merchants outfitted it, and the brothers also intended to go along. When they were ready for sailing Kor-

mák rode to visit Steingerd, and before they parted, Kormák
very leisurely planted two kisses on Steingerd's cheek. Tintein would not stand for that. Friends of both parties went
between and agreed that Kormák would have to pay damages.
Kormák asked what they asked in payment.

Thorvald said: "The two rings which I lost before."

Then Kormák spoke this verse:

> 76. Paid I with pair of rings the
> price of hugging twice—be-
> fell you[1] that before—his
> Frigg-of-precious-jewels.[2]
> Never cost two kisses,
> comely woman, me more—I'll
> cruelly miss her kiss and
> converse sweet—than those two!

And when Kormák was ready to board his ship he spoke
this verse:

> 77. Borne shall be, before on
> board we go, this verse of
> mine to Sif-of-silk[3] in
> Svínadale who loves me;
> come to her ears shall all that
> e'er I said: that to me
> was the lady linen-dight
> liefer than my own self.

Then Kormák and his brother Thorgils sailed away from
Iceland and joined the court of the king (of Norway). They
were well received there.

We are told that Steingerd asked Thorvald Tintein to go
abroad with her. He said it was not advisable, yet could not
deny it to her. They set out on their journey and crossed the
sea, and vikings fell upon them and wanted to rob them and
abduct Steingerd. Kormák got wind of that. He came up and
stood by them so that they kept all their goods. Then they arrived at the king's court; and one day when Kormák was

walking on the street[4] he saw Steingerd sitting in a house and went up to it to talk with her, and gave her four kisses. Thorvald saw it and drew his sword. Women went between them, and word was sent to King Harold. He declared it would be difficult to keep watch on them; "but I shall make peace between you." They agreed to that.

The king said: "One kiss is offset by Kormák's lending you assistance (when you were attacked) at landing, and another, by Kormák's rescuing Steingerd; but the two remaining kisses are to be compensated by two ounces of gold."

Kormák then spoke the same verse that was set down before:

(76). Paid I with pair of rings . . .

One day when Kormák was walking on the street he saw Steingerd. He went up to her and asked her to go with him. Thereupon he snatched her up, but she cried out for help. The king happened to be near and approached. He thought these to be strange proceedings. He took her away from him and spoke sharply to him. The king took it in ill part. Nevertheless Kormák stayed at the court and quickly regained the king's favor, and the winter passed quietly.

XXV · KORMÁK FELLS THORVALD ON AN EXPEDITION WITH KING HAROLD

IN THE spring after, the king prepared to undertake a large expedition to the land of the Permians.[1] Kormák was in command of one ship on that expedition, and Thorvald, of another. No other skippers are mentioned. And when the two sailed close by one another in a certain sound, Kormák struck Thorvald on the head with his tiller so that he fell down senseless by the rudder. Kormák's ship then sheared off as it

was rudderless. Steingerd had been sitting by Thorvald's
side. She took over the rudder and steered straight at Kormák's ship. Kormák saw that and spoke this verse:

> 78.[2] Fast now fell my blow on the
> fellow's middle head-piece
> with the tiller—tagged that
> Tintein after the woman:
> struck, he staggered back on
> stern-post of the sea-steed.
> Steer not at me, Steingerd,
> sternly though you threaten!

His ship capsized with him and his men, but all were
quickly rescued as many were near. Thorvald came to again,
and they proceeded on their journey. The king offered to be
umpire in the matter, and both agreed to that. He decreed
that the treatment Kormák had received (in having his ship
overturned) offset the blow he had dealt Thorvald.

They made land in the evening, and the king and his men
sat and ate their meal there. Kormák sat toward the outside
at the door of the tent and drank together with Steingerd out
of the same vessel. While he was doing that some man stole
Kormák's cloak-pin[3] to make sport of him. Kormák had laid
his cloak aside, and when he wanted to put it on again the
cloak-pin was gone. Kormák sprang up and ran after the man
with his spear Vígr and hurled it at him but missed.

Then he spoke this verse:

> 79. Robbed my clasp the wretched
> rogue as I drank to Steingerd.
> Surely shall I nowise
> share it[4] like two youngsters.
> Shafted well is Vígr, but
> widely I did miss him:
> it dug a divot up and
> deeply stuck in moss-bank.

Thereupon they traveled on to Perm and back from there,
and returned to Norway.

XXVI · KORMÁK RESCUES STEINGERD FROM VIKINGS

THORVALD TINTEIN made his ship ready to sail to Denmark, and Steingerd went with him. A short time afterwards the two brothers (Kormák and Thorgils) journeyed the same way and arrived late one evening at the Brenn Islands.[1] There they saw Thorvald's ship before them. He was there himself, and some men with him. They had been robbed of all their possessions by vikings, and Steingerd had been abducted by them. The chief of the vikings was Thorstein, the son of Ásmund (Ash-Side) who had fought with Ogmund, the father of Kormák and Thorgils.

Thorvald and Kormák met, and Kormák asked whether ill had befallen them. He replied: "Matters have indeed taken an ill turn."

Kormák asked: "What has happened, has Steingerd left you?"

Thorvald answered: "Steingerd is gone and all our property."

Kormák said: "Why don't you try to recover her and what else you lost?"

Thorvald replied: "We do not have a sufficient force to do so."

Kormák said: "So you admit that you are not equal to the occasion?"

Thorvald said: "We are no match for Thorstein; but if you have the strength, then fight for her and keep her."

Kormák said: "Then we shall try."

At night the two brothers took a boat and rowed over to the viking ship. They climbed up into Thorstein's ship. Steingerd was on the raised afterdeck and had fallen to the share of a man;[2] but most of the crew were on land and had made a fire to warm themselves. Kormák had picked up what he wanted to know from the cooks, and they had told him all the brothers wanted to know. They boarded the ship by the stern gangway. Thorgils seized the man who was to have Steingerd and hauled him on deck, and Kormák killed him against the

side of the ship. Thorgils leaped overboard with Steingerd
and swam to land. When Kormák had almost reached the
shore many eels[3] wound themselves around his arms and legs
so that he was drawn under. Then Kormák spoke this verse:

> 80. Warriors! Worms a-plenty
> went for me, the time I,
> swimming o'er the sea, did
> seek to free the woman:
> fain, if in that fray had
> fallen the son of Ogmund—
> saved I the silken-Sif[4] from
> sorrow—I'd be remembered.[5]

Kormák swam to land and returned Steingerd to Thorvald. Then Thorvald told Steingerd to go with Kormák. He
said he had rescued her manfully. Kormák said that would
suit him well. But Steingerd said she did not care to change
her state (in that fashion). And Kormák also thought that
fate would hardly grant them (to live together) and said that
evil spirits, or else a contrary fate, had prevented that from
the start.
He spoke this verse:

> 81. Strive not, Gerd-of-golden-
> girdle,[6] to suit my wishes:
> little you know—with the lout shalt
> lie!—what is best for me.
> Howbeit, Hlín-of-antique-
> head-dress,[7] thou shalt henceforth—
> Ódin's-drink[8] I dealt you—
> dwell now with the booby.

Kormák bade Steingerd stay with her husband.

XXVII · KORMÁK FALLS IN SCOTLAND

THEREUPON the brothers returned to Norway, but Thorvald Tintein sailed to Iceland. The two brothers harried in

Ireland, Wales, England, and Scotland and acquired fame
as redoubtable warriors. They founded the fortress of
Skarthaborg[1] (Scarborough). Then they harried into Scotland and did great deeds and had a numerous company. In
that host no one equalled Kormák in strength and daring.

One time, after they had harried, Kormák pursued the foe,
but the others had returned to the ship. Then out of the
woods came an uncanny Scottish giant,[2] and a fierce struggle
began. Kormák was inferior to him in strength, and the giant
was made more powerful by magic. Kormák looked for his
sword, but it had left the sheath. He stretched out his hand to
reach it and gave the giant a death blow. But the giant grap-
pled so hard with Kormák that his ribs were staved in and he
fell, and the dead giant on top of him, so that Kormák could
not get up. After a while his men went to look for him and
brought him to the ships.

Then Kormák spoke this verse:

> 82. 'Twas not like straining Steingerd,
>   steerer-of-ships, in your
>   arms, when in the fray I
>   empty-handed battled.
>   At eve, his ale would drink in
>   Odin's hall[3]—sooth say I—
>   the skald unless from scabbard
>   Skrýmir had leaped and helped me.[4]

Then they attended to Kormák's wounds and found that
the ribs in both his sides were broken. Kormák said he did
not require any bandages. He lay wounded for some time,
and his men grieved that he had proceeded so incautiously.
Kormák spoke this verse:

> 83. Hoped I had before, thou
>   Hlín-of-armrings,[5] grimly,
>   in strife that cold steel would
>   stave off dying of sickness.
>   'Scape yet hath the skald none—
>   scatheless few men live un-
>   doomed in pangs of pain to
>   perish—but die a straw-death.

And again:

> 84. Was not with me, arm-fair
>   woman, your spouse, the time we—
>   fresh blood flowed from spoil there—
>   fought that morn in Ireland,
>   sheath-drawn when the shatterer-
>   of-shields[6] did sing, gold-Sága,[7]
>   about my beard—the raven's
>   beak was gore-besprinkled.

Then his strength began to wane. He spoke this verse:

> 85. Dew-of-wounds[8] from deep cuts
>   down rushed from our sword-blades:
>   bore I with the best a
>   bloody sword on foreshore.
>   Broadest brands then wielded
>   briskest trees-of-combat;[9]
>   yet must I, Gerd-of-golden-
>   girdles, die a straw-death.

Kormák said he wished to make over to his brother Thorgils both his property and his followers, because he loved him most to enjoy them. Then Kormák died, and Thorgils took over his followers and was in viking expeditions for a long time.

And herewith ends this saga.

THE SWORN BROTHERS'
SAGA

INTRODUCTION

THE saga of the Sworn Brothers, Thorgeir and Thormód, occupies a position of secondary importance among the Old Icelandic family sagas—at least, it is not a favorite. There are good reasons for this: it does not have the scope and weight of such sagas as *Njála, Eigla, Laxdœla,* nor the depth and classic form of such as *Hrafnkels saga, Gísla saga, Thorsteins saga hvíta;* nor do students of Germanic antiquities value it because of any wealth of specific information on the history, religion, culture, laws of the Old North. Nevertheless, it should rightfully take its place among the "biographic" sagas of skalds and warriors such as those of Kormák, Gunnlaug, and Hallfred because, though fairly discursive, it is effectively held together by our interest in the fate and character of Thormód as the loyal sworn-brother, the resourceful adventurer, the lover, the skald; and a romantic flavor is added by his touching devotion to the cause and person of Holy King Ólaf. Chiefly, though, the memory of Thormód lives in the North through his skald's role in the Battle of Stiklastad and his last heroic moments.

Superficially, the saga is seen to fall into four distinct parts—the early lives of the sworn-brothers, the amours of Thormód, the fall of Thorgeir and the revenge taken for it in Greenland, and Thormód's life and death with King Ólaf. But a longer occupation with the saga reveals a greater inner coherence and a deeper meaning, perhaps, than the author himself realized or, at any rate, expressed. This is but natural, however; for, after all, sagas were told by the *gleðimaðr* to entertain his audience, and not to exemplify or elaborate a problem, as the serious modern reader would require of great art. We, on the contrary, seem to see in the saga the story of a man who is not satisfied with the normal course and tasks of life: Thormód is not "sufficient unto himself." He craves to fill his life with greater meaning. This he finds, while young, in thoughtless adventures and in following his sworn-brother Thorgeir, who is, indeed, a leader but who has no such cravings; and in his absence, in shallow amours. But when Thorgeir is slain, life is given a deeper purpose for Thormód by the call to revenge, which he executes with savage single-mindedness. After it is accomplished he seeks, and finds, a purpose in life through faithful service to Ólaf, the missionary king of Norway. Thereafter, when Ólaf, in the conception of that age, suffers a martyr's death, life can hold no further meaning to Thormód and he courts the fatal arrow in order to be reunited with his beloved king in heaven.

It may be thought that the modern mind reads all this "into" the story. As a fact, however, Thormód's is a complex character, with a poet's instability. Unlike the sullen Thorgeir, the gifted young man seeks women's company—he cannot endure the boredom on his father's farm or of his boorish boatmates, and still less the loneliness of a cave in Greenland, which he leaves at the risk of his life. He is attracted by the physical charms of Thordís, but even more so by the pleasing ways and interesting mind of Thorbiorg—Coal-Brow—in whose praise he indites verses and as whose poet he was, and still is, widely known. He denies her, though, and lies shamelessly to regain the favors of Thorbiorg; but he has also the manhood to stand up against King Canute's peremptoriness.

Woman's love is, indeed, desirable to him, but it is not a consuming passion as with a Kormák; and, like some other mercurial skalds, he eschews marriage. To him, it would mean "settling down" for good to the humdrum existence of a farmer. There were other means for satisfying desires: in Greenland (if we may read between the lines) he becomes involved in a purely sensual affair with a serving woman; which leads to a sordid rivalry with her bedfellow and ultimately costs him the friendship and assistance of powerful Thorkel Leifsson and thus involves increased danger in carrying out his revenge. Though willing to follow the reckless Thorgeir in any escapade, Thormód, seeing farther than he, refuses to pit himself against his sworn-brother. He knows full well that any rivalry would destroy their brotherhood, which is sacred to him; indeed, might lead to outright enmity. And the author has, rather skillfully, inserted into his story the warning example of the gay foster-brothers, Eyólf and Thorgeir Spendthrift, who fall out for a trifling matter and slay each other in blind fury. Rather than risk such an outcome, Thormód chooses to leave his sworn-brother.

There is a tantalizing hint in Thorgil's remark at the Althing that Thormód feared God.[1] The heathen Scandinavians were not afraid of their gods. If the remark is authentic, it suggests that Thormód, even before joining King Ólaf and thus inevitably being baptized, had somehow come under the influence of Christianity, which could not possibly have reached him when a youth. Thorgeir, on the other hand, very evidently believed only in his own might and strength (*i mátt sinn ok megin*). His is a typical viking nature with its overbearing self-reliance and lack of any gentler traits and tastes. He is not without chivalry, however, and a certain self-righteousness, which furnishes him moralizing saws to justify his own self-appointed distributing of the goods of others. In extenuation of his many bloody deeds it may be said that they were all done under provocation,[2] when the old Germanic code of honor demanded retaliation.

Beside these foreground figures the many other characters, from king down to beggarman, play roles hardly even of the second rank. Some are types rather than individuals. Thus the humorously conceived beldames, aggressive matchmakers, and good hands at magic, all of them; the staunch and resourceful friends, Skúf and Biarni; the hot-headed farmers Jodur and Snorri; the lively young bloods Eyólf and Thorgeir Spendthrift. Best conceived, certainly, and not without merit, is the little genre picture of the timorous, stingy old couple housing and feeding the two fighting cocks, Thorgeir and Butraldi; least satisfactory, because unrealistic, the figure of Gest who boards the ship—Greenland-bound with

---

[1] See Appendix I. The word *guðhræddr* means more than our "god-fearing." But that Thormód was no fanatic is shown by the following anecdote (*Flateyarbók* II, 336): Once on a fast day he was hungry and took and ate half a sausage. When rebuked he made the sensible reply that it would require more than a piece of sausage to have Christ and him fall out.

[2] Barring two, probably apocryphal, anecdotes of wanton manslaughter by him (*Flateyarbók* II, 105, 107) not here printed.

Thormód, as another avenger of Thorgeir, though we are nowhere told on what provocation—who exhibits the traits,
familiar through the *fornaldarsǫgur*, of Ódin walking the
earth in disguise. A pity that the motivation is so meager in
the case of the jealous but noble-minded slave Kolbak and the
likewise jealous but brutal slave Lodin. But then, practically
all sagas teem with comic and tragic figures whose physiog-
nomy is drawn only in the sketchiest fashion and thus leave
a wealth of raw material for the modern novelist!

There is excellent story telling, on the whole, even though
the main argument is much diluted with poorly integrated
material, both from local tradition and the invention of the
narrator. To the former we must reckon such unrelated episodes as that of Grettir escaping the noose, the thefts of Veglág, the appearance of the ghosts of Thorgeir and his men,
the account of Helgi the White and his fight with Thorstein
Egilsson, even the tragic tale of the two foster-brothers.
Whereas the magic as well as the names of Katla and the two
Grímas, the similarly inscenated slayings of Jodur and Thórir,
the similarly handled bribing of Vermund and of skipper Ingolf, the nearly identical dreams of (the Greenlandish)
Thordís and Gríma, all may confidently be set down as belonging to the bag of tricks at the disposal of the routine saga
teller.

A similar observation can be made with regard to the
speeches in which the saga abounds : some of the shorter ones
no doubt were handed down by tradition, many more have
elements common to the repertory of the saga narrator. The
author makes the most of a number of trite situations, such
as wordy, trifling servants answering a knock at the door or
refusing to get up at night to answer it. But he is a master as
well of the stinging repartee and of the difficult art of advanc-
ing the action through dialogue. We may safely credit him
with all exchanges of words such as those between Thorgeir
and Jodur, Thorgils Mársson, Thórir, Ingolf Sulky—all in
the usual laconic saga manner, yet admirable in their swift,
inexorable progress culminating in the *ultima ratio*. And the
evasive speeches of the two Grímas—both expert liars in

what seems to them a good cause—are pearls of tart humor and the *tu quoque* argument.

Above, I have spoken of "the author." Not a single author of the many Icelandic family sagas has named himself. We know why: like the authors of the continental folk epics he considered himself a transmitter, or gatherer, of traditions rather than a creator. Yet, of course, sagas do not, any more than epics or folk songs, compose themselves. There always was some person whose interest in traditions caused him to gather and, according to his ability, weld his material into a more or less coherent whole if not into artistic unity. We know that such interest was especially marked in Iceland during the *ritǫld* (Writing Age) from about the middle of the twelfth century to about 1300.

In case the remark in the *Mǫðruvallabók* version, that the hall erected by Thorgeir on Reykianess still stood in 1233, was the author's own, then the saga was committed to parchment, say, in the middle of the thirteenth century (because we must suppose that such a notice must refer to recently past time). However, copyists were given to bringing their manuscripts "up to date." General considerations, and more specifically the fact that Abbot Styrmir seems to have known the story of Thormód's end when he wrote his history of Saint Ólaf (about 1220), make it more likely that the saga in some form existed already at the beginning of the thirteenth century. Such an earlier date would well agree with the probable dates of other sagas dealing with personages of the northwestern part of the island.

That the author had his home there is amply evident from his remarkably accurate knowledge of the intricate topography of that land of firths and mountains. Add to this his interest, shown in passages organically connected with the narrative, in the existence of churches and the state of Christianity at the time in both Greenland and Iceland, and we are bound to infer that he was a cleric connected, perhaps, with the nearby cloister of Thingeyrar whose office would require him to visit many localities in his diocese where he could talk with parishioners and gather their traditions and also indulge his preoccupation with antiquarian topography[3]; whereas, we may note by the way, he is not much interested in the genealogical lore and the details of legal procedure which fill so many pages of the sagas, somewhat to their detriment as artistic creations. Thingeyrar, the oldest of Icelandic cloisters, founded in the beginning of the twelfth century, long maintained a considerable literary activity dealing with secular as well as religious subjects: the clerics of Iceland always were more nationally minded than those of the continent.

We do not possess the saga in its original form. The manuscripts in which it is preserved all show adventitious elements; moreover the two main manuscripts are defective: the *Hauksbók* version, contained in the great collection of sagas, poems, and other material compiled by the prominent Icelander, Hauk Erlendsson, in the first part of the fourteenth century, lacks the beginning up to Chapter XI, several layers of pages of the codex having dropped out; and the *Mǫðruvallabók* version (written ca. 1350), eked out by a copy made of it early in the eighteenth century, when more of it was left, carries us only to the quarrel of Thorgeir and Gest on board ship (Chapter XX). Besides, we have the whole saga in its latest and most expanded form in the giant compilation of the *Flateyarbók* (written ca. 1390), where it constitutes portions of the saga of Saint Ólaf—from which the pieces given in the Appendices are taken—as well as a number of other fragments and paper manuscripts. There can be little doubt that of all these, the *Hauksbók* version comes closest to the original,[4] while the others, and especially the one contained in the *Flateyarbók*, have been dilated by much verbiage and augmented with scraps of local tradition. It is on some interpolator—a

---

[3] Cf. the information on Hvítastaðir (p. 122) and Smithy Ridge (p. 110) which could have been gathered only by personal visits to the spot. It would be difficult to say whether the account of the topography and cultural conditions of Greenland at the time is due to personal acquaintance or to an unusually reliable tradition.

[4] However, according to Sven B. F. Jansson, *Sagorna om Vinland* i (1944), pp. 172ff, the first part of the saga to Chap. xix incl., copied by Hauk himself, shows clear indications of shortening.

cleric, no doubt—that we can blame the curious malaprop rhetorical, theological, and physiological digressions, all in the "learned" style, which stick out from the unassuming, athletic style of the groundwork of the saga like a sore thumb —in fact, are unique in saga literature. And while sagas in general refrain from commenting on men and their actions, this interpolator plainly shows his admiration for Thorgeir's prowess and is amusingly anxious to reconcile the manly but heathen virtues of his hero with the teachings of Christianity.

The present translation follows the *Mǫðruvallabók* so far as it goes, beyond where it overlaps the *Hauksbók* version, then follows the latter. My reason for so doing is the observation that the prolixities and interpolations of the *Mǫðruvallabók* grow notably less as the saga progresses; so that when it gives out, the change over to the style of *Hauksbók* is almost insensible. Both manuscript versions are available now for easy comparison, with the variations and additions of *Flateyarbók*, in the critical edition of Björn K. Thórólfsson for the *Samfund for Udgivelse af gammel Nordisk Litteratur*, Copenhagen, 1925-1927, and in Vol. VI of the *Fornritafélag* edition, 1943.

THORMÓD'S POETRY

Some forty stanzas, apparently all genuine, have come down to us from the skaldship of Thormód—which is a relatively large amount, allowing us to take the measure of his ability. As is the case with all skalds, a major portion of his production must have been lost, else it would be difficult to account for the technical mastery of the intricate *dróttkvætt* measure[5] evinced in what we have. Most regrettable, and hard to explain, is the complete disappearance of the *Kolbrúnar vísur*, composed in honor of Thorbiorg of Arnardale —her of the coal-brows—because, as remarked, Thormód was, and still is, widely famed in the North just for these. If

[5] Except for poor transmission in some cases. The existence of a large number of variant readings, at times comprising whole lines, is proof that Thormód's verses were frequently recited.

we had them our saga would be more nearly a parallel to the biographic sagas of the other erotic poets of Iceland.[6]

Thormód hardly ranks with the hǫfuðskǫld, such great poets as Egil, Sigvat, Arnór, principally because he lacks originality, both of style and conception. Although inspired by deep loyalty to his sworn-brother, his *Thorgeirs drápa* is not memorable in any way. Distinctly more interesting are his *lausavísur* (verses spoken on occasion) which, properly understood, lighten the narrative of the saga. I would single out stanza 19, in which a point is neatly turned in the last line; and stanzas 21, 25, 28, where a certain grim humor lifts the verses over the average phraseology. And it is fair to say that in stanzas 30 and 31 the poet's fervid devotion to his king lends him a passionate intensity reminding us of Skaldic art at its best. The last five stanzas, composed, we are told, impromptu by a man wounded unto death, show that heroism was not a mere pose with Thormód. Altogether, though, one is forced to admit that the impressive account of the skald's last hours, especially as told by Snorri in his *Heimskringla*, has shed glory on Thormód's poetry. Nor should we forget his fame as a reciter, which led King Ólaf to select him to rouse his army on the fatal day of Stiklastad with some poem: "Whereupon (according to Snorri, *ibid.*, Chap. 208) Thormód recited the *Old Lay of Biarki* so loud that all the army could hear it."

6 Cf. Hollander, *The Skalds*, Chap. 6.

I · THORBIORG SAVES GRETTIR FROM THE NOOSE

IN THE DAYS of holy King Ólaf[1] there were many chieftains under his rule, not only in Norway but in all lands over which he had sway. [And all those who were most worthy in the sight of God were also those in whom the king found greatest pleasure.][2] At that time there lived a noted chieftain in Iceland, in the Ice Firth district, whose name was Vermund. He was the son of Thorgrím and[3] the brother of Víga-Styr. Vermund had his dwelling in the Water Firth. He was a wise and well-liked man. His wife was called Thorbiorg and nicknamed Thorbiorg the Stout. She was a keen-witted woman and of a domineering disposition. Whenever Vermund was not at home she had charge of the district and the people in it; and all thought their affairs well taken care of by her.

It so happened, once when Vermund was not at home, that Grettir Ásmundsson[4] came to the Ice Firth district. It was at the time he had been made an outlaw. And wherever he went most people gave him whatever he chose to have; and though he termed the things they let him have presents, the fact is that they would not have been given if people had not stood in mortal terror of him. Therefore the farmers gathered together and took him captive. They condemned him to death and raised a gallows to hang him.

When Thorbiorg learned of their intention she went with her man-servants to the gathering which had sentenced him and arrived just when the gallows had been erected and the noose fixed and Grettir was led up to it. They delayed only when they saw Thorbiorg approaching. She asked the men in the gathering what they meant to do, and they told her.

She said: "It seems unwise to me to put him to death, because he has important kinsmen and is remarkable for his strength and many achievements, even though he has not been fortunate in every respect. His kinsmen would deplore his loss, although many have found it hard to get along with him."

The men replied: "It seems to us that he deserves death, because he has been declared an outlaw[5] and is guilty of robbery."

Thorbiorg said: "He is not going to be put to death this time if I have anything to say."

They said: "You have the power to prevent us from putting him to death, whether that is just or not."

Then Thorbiorg had Grettir released and gave him his life and told him to go where he would. About this incident Grettir made the following ditty:

1. My head then
   had I quickly
   to stick in noose
   knotted for me,
   if Thorbiorg,
   that wise woman,
   had not saved
   the singer in time.

From this incident it will appear how notable a person she was.

II · THORGEIR AND THORMÓD AND THEIR KINSFOLK. JODUR KILLS THORGEIR'S FATHER

A CERTAIN MAN by the name of Hávar, the son of Klepp, lived on a farm called Glacier Spring. Hávar's kinsfolk lived south on Alftaness, but he had left that neighborhood on account of some manslaughters which he had committed there; for he was a great fighter, of a brawling disposition and hard to get along with. His wife was called Thórelfr. She came from the Broad Firth and was the daughter of Álf from the Dales, a prominent and excellent man. Hávar and Thórelfr had a son called Thorgeir. He was mature early, of great stature, powerfully built and headstrong. Already when a boy he learned the use of arms and how to shield himself.

Bersi was the name of a man who lived in the Ice Firth district, on the farm called Dyrdil Moor.[1] His wife was Thorgerd, and their son was called Thormód. Already at an early age he was of a brisk and courageous disposition. He was of middle height and had black, curly hair.[2]

At that time there lived on the farm Reykiahólar[3] on Reykianess a great chieftain called Thorgils Arason, a man wise and well liked, powerful and upright. Illugi was the name of his brother, who was a retainer of King Ólaf the Saint. Illugi made many trading journeys and spent the winters, now with King Ólaf, now in Reykiahólar. He had brought from Norway timber both for a church and a hall.

The brothers, Thorgils and Illugi, were the sons of Ari Ólafsson, the son of Ulf the Squinter who took possession of Reykianess. He, again, was a son of Hogni the White, the son of Ótrygg, the son of Óblaud, the son of King Hiorleif.[4] Thorgerd was the mother of Thorgils and Illugi, and she was the daughter of Álf from the Dales. Álf's mother was Hild, the daughter of Thorstein the Red, the son of Óleif the White, the son of Ingiald,[4] the son of Fródi, whose mother was Thóra, the daughter of Sigurd Snake-in-the-Eye; and the mother of Sigurd was Áslaug, the daughter of Sigurd the Slayer of Fáfnir.

Thorgeir Hávarsson was (as we have seen) the cousin of Thorgils Arason. Thorgeir and Thormód both grew up in the Ice Firth district, and there soon arose friendship between them; because in many respects they were similar to each other in disposition. [Soon, too, they surmised—which, indeed, came to be true—that they would both die a violent death, because neither was minded ever to give in, with whomsoever they had to deal. They ever thought more of success in this life than of the glorious joys in the life to come.] Therefore they swore oaths to one another that whichever lived longer was to avenge the death of the other. [For though people called themselves Christians, their Christianity was still young and weak, so that many traces of heathendom remained and entered into their customs. Thus it had been the practice of illustrious men who made a covenant between them, that he who survived should avenge the other;] and in confirmation thereof they went under three strips of sod. The ceremony was performed in this wise that three long pieces of sod were cut so that their ends were fast to the ground and the loops raised up so that the men could walk through under them. By this ceremony, Thormód and Thorgeir confirmed their oaths.[5]

Thormód was a little older, yet Thorgeir was the stronger of the two. Soon they made themselves a name. They ranged far and wide about the countryside and were ill liked. Many asserted that they behaved with great overbearing. They had the help and support of their fathers, as was to be expected, and many men thought they confirmed them in their evil ways. And those who considered themselves to have suffered loss at the hands of the sworn-brothers went to see Vermund and requested him to rid them of this trouble.

Vermund summoned Hávar and Bersi and told them that the behavior of their sons had aroused great displeasure. "You, Hávar, are from outside the district and have settled here without anybody's leave. So far, we have not objected to your dwelling here; but now your son Thorgeir is causing trouble and disturbance. It is our wish, therefore, that you remove yourself and your possessions from the Ice Firth. As to Bersi and his son, we shall not drive them away, because they are settled in this district. Also, we expect less disturbance from Thormód once he and Thorgeir are separated."

Hávar said: "It lies in your power, Vermund, to make us leave the Ice Firth with our possessions. However, I don't know but Thorgeir is going to decide for himself where he will stay."

In accordance with this decision, Hávar removed to the Borgar Firth and lived at the place which now is called Hávar's Homestead. Thorgeir then lived, sometimes with his father and sometimes west[6] in the Ice Firth district with Thormód, and was to many a most unwelcome visitor although he was only a youth. For a long time he stayed at

Reykjahólar with his kinsman Thorgils and stood in favor with him. He and Ari, the son of Thorgils, were great friends, and that remained so as long as they lived.

There was a man called Jodur who lived on the farm Skelia-brekka. He was a fearless man, a chieftain, hard to get along with, unfair in his dealings with many. He was a power in the district, ambitious, and a great man-slayer who rarely made atonement for those he had slain. It so happened one winter that Jodur and his man-servants journeyed to Akra-ness⁷ to buy flour. On the way he came to Hávar and asked to borrow a horse for the trip to Akraness.

Hávar loaned him the horse but said: "I shall ask you to leave the horse here on your return and not to keep it longer."

Jodur agreed to that. He rode to Akraness and bought flour, as was his intention, and returned when he had at-tended to his needs. And when he was riding back along the Grunna Firth past Hávar's farm, his men reminded him that they were to go up to the farm and return the horse.

Jodur said: "I don't care to be delayed by that. I am going to lead the horse with its load to my farm and send it back when I have used it for my purposes."

They said: "You may do as you please, but Hávar never yet put up with anyone who does not stick to what he agreed to."

"There is no help for that now," said Jodur.

Hávar saw the men passing by and recognized them. He went out to meet them and greeted them and said: "Now you will have to leave that horse here."

Jodur said: "You will surely let me lead it home with me to Skeliabrekka?"

Hávar said: "I do not care to have the horse go any far-ther."

Jodur said: "We are going to use the horse even though you won't loan it."

Hávar said: "I don't know about that."

He ran up to the horse and knocked off the packs and took the horse by the bridle to lead it back. Jodur had a barbed spear in his hand. He went at Hávar with it and ran

him through, and that was his death. Then Jodur took the
horse and led it along and went his way till he came home.
Now Hávar's homefolks wondered about his staying out so
long. They searched for him and found him dead on the spot
where he was slain. They thought it a most dreadful occurrence.

Thorgeir was in the Ice Firth district at that time. The report of the slaying of Hávar quickly spread through the district. [And when Thorgeir learned of his father's death he
showed no signs of emotion. His face did not flush, for his
anger did not mount to his skin; neither did he grow pale, for
his rage did not pierce his breast; nor did he become livid,
for his wrath did not enter his bones. Rather, he showed no
sign of emotion at the report, for his heart was not like the
crop of a bird, nor was it full of blood so that it trembled with
fear; but on the contrary it was hardened by the All-highest
Creator for all deeds of daring.][8]

III · THORGEIR AVENGES HIS FATHER'S DEATH. THORGEIR AND THORMÓD WITH THE WIDOW SIGRFLIÓD

[WE ARE TOLD that Thorgeir had little to do with women.
He thought it a debasement of his strength to make up to
them. He laughed but seldom and generally was unfriendly
with people. He was of great stature, manly in appearance,
and had huge strength. Thorgeir owned an axe, large and
shaped like a halberd. It was keen-edged and sharp, and many
a man got his night's shelter under it.[1] He also had a big flat-
bladed battle-axe with a hard point and cutting edges, and its
socket was large and the shaft thick. At that time swords
were not much used for weapons in Iceland.]

When Thorgeir had learned of his father's death he went

to Reykiahólar to visit Thorgils. He told him that he intended to journey south to the Borgar Firth in order to see his mother and requested Thorgils to furnish the means to cross the Broad Firth. Thorgils complied with his wishes, and he went south to the Borgar Firth. We are not told where he passed the nights. The traveling was good, no snow had fallen in the district, and all water courses were frozen over. When he had crossed the White River he made his way to Skeliabrekka. The weather was foggy and mild, and it was dark, both on account of the fog and approaching night. He arrived at the place late in the evening, and when he came up to the buildings the doors were closed, and the people had just come into the living room from the kitchen.[2] A light burned in the living room.

Thorgeir knocked at the door. Jodur said: "Someone is knocking. Let one of the servants go out."

Then one of the servants looked out and saw a man standing outside the door all armed. He asked who he was.

Thorgeir answered: "Vígfús[3] is my name."

The man-servant said: "Come in, you can have a night's lodging here."

Thorgeir said: "I will not accept hospitality from a slave— bid Jodur come out."

The servant went back while Thorgeir remained standing outside, and Jodur asked the man as he returned into the living room: "Who was it outside?"

The servant answered: "How can I know since he doesn't seem to know himself?" Jodur asked: "Didn't you ask him to stay here?"

The man answered: "Yes, I did."

Jodur said: "And what did he answer?"

"He said he would not accept hospitality from a slave, and that you should come out."

Jodur seized his spear and put his helmet on his head and went to the door with two of his men-servants. He saw a man standing before the door. He lowered his spear, resting its point on the threshold. He asked who was the man who had come.

The answer was: "My name is Thorgeir."

Jodur said: "What Thorgeir?"

"I am the son of Hávar."

Jodur said: "And what is your business here?"

Thorgeir answered: "I don't know as yet how it will turn out, but I have come to ask what reparation you will make for the killing of my father Hávar."

Jodur said: "I don't know whether you have heard that I have slain many a man and never yet made any reparation."

"That is news to me," said Thorgeir, "but whatever may be true about that, it is my business now to learn what reparation you will make for this slaying, for you have struck down my closest kinsman."

Jodur said: "I am by no means opposed to listen to your claims; but I shall make no amends for this slaying, Thorgeir, because others might then think they were entitled to reparations."

Thorgeir answered: "It rests with you to decide what reparations you will make to others, but I shall have to decide in my case."

During this exchange of words Thorgeir had been standing at a little distance from the door. He had a spear in his right hand, with the point held forward, and an axe in his right. It was hard for Jodur and his men to distinguish things outside as they came from the light, but Thorgeir could see a little better those who stood in the doorway. And when they least expected it Thorgeir went up to the door and thrust Jodur through his middle so that he fell into the arms of his servants in the doorway. Thorgeir quickly vanished into the darkness of the night while the servants were busy about Jodur. Thorgeir was fifteen years old when this took place as Thormód says in the memorial poem (*drápa*)[4] he composed about him:

> 2. This the first of feats, that
>   fell by his hands—was the
>   sea-steed's[5] steerer young though
>   stout-souled—Klœng's son Jodur:

brought about his father's
banesman's death—his under-
takings lacked not luck—the
lad when fifteen winters.

Thorgeir continued on his way during the night and did not stop till he arrived at Hávar's Homestead. There he knocked at the door, and it was some time before someone came. Thorelfr called on one of her man-servants to go to the door. He awoke, rubbing his eyes, and complained about having to get up.

He said: "I shouldn't think it necessary to go to the door even if someone does come at night."

Thorelfr said: "Only one who is compelled by necessity would be going about in this pitch darkness."

"I don't know about that," said the servant, and he got up rather slowly and went to the door.[6] He saw a man standing outside in the darkness. He did not greet him but went back to his bed and lay down and covered himself up. Thorgeir went in, closing the door after him, and turned to go into the living room.

Thorelfr asked: "Who is it came?"

The servant said: "I neither know nor care who he is."

She said: "A mighty indifferent man you are, indeed!" Then she called to a woman-servant: "You get up and go to the living room and find out who came in."

The woman got up and went to the living room, opening the door to it just a little, and asked if anyone was there.

The answer came: "There certainly is."

She asked who it was, and he answered: "I am Thorgeir." She closed the door again and went back into the sleeping room.

Thorelfr asked: "Well, who is it?"

The maid answered: "I think it is your son Thorgeir."

Then Thorelfr arose and made a light. She went into the living room and welcomed her son. She asked him what had happened.

Thorgeir said: "Someone was wounded this evening at Skeliabrekka."

Thorelfr said: "Was it any of your doings?"

Thorgeir answered: "I will not deny it."

Thorelfr said: "How big a wound was it?"

Thorgeir answered: "I don't think the wound he got from me will need a bandage. I saw that my spear went right through him, and he fell back into the arms of his servants."

Then Thorelfr said with joy in her heart: "This is no boy's deed. Thanks to you for the doing of it. But why did not the followers of Jodur pursue you?"

Thorgeir answered: "They had other work to attend to. Besides, they quickly lost sight of me in the dark of night."

Thorelfr said: "Very likely."

Then they gave Thorgeir his supper. And when he had had all he wanted Thorelfr said: "My advice is that you lie down to sleep now, but get up before morning and ride west to the Broad Firth.[7] My men-servants shall accompany you as far as you wish. People will come here in the morning to look for you, and I do not have the power to hold you against so many. Also, the water courses will open up soon if this thaw lasts, and then the going will be more difficult. You have done here what was most needful to do. Bring our kinsman Thorgils the message that he must provide me with some homestead out west in his neighborhood. I shall sell my land here and move to the district I came from."

Thorgeir did as his mother advised him. He went to sleep, and got up early in the morning and rode away. Nothing is said about his journey till he arrived at the Broad Firth. There he got him a boat and on it reached Reykianess in the west.[8] There he related the slaying of Jodur. To all who heard of the occurrence it seemed a marvelous thing that a mere youth should have been the death of so powerful a chieftain and so great a fighter as was Jodur. [And yet it was not strange, because the Creator of All had formed, and laid in Thorgeir's breast, so fierce and undaunted a heart that he was not afraid; and he was as fearless in all tests of courage as is the lion. And since all good qualities are from God, also fearlessness is from God, and put into the hearts of fearless men, and therewith a free will, to do as they list, whether good or evil. Because Christ has made Christians his sons but not his slaves. But to each he gives according to his acts.]

After that Thorgeir stayed, now at Reykiahólar, now out west[9] in the Ice Firth. In the spring following these events Thorelfr moved west[9] to Reykianess with all her possessions. The same summer, an agreement was reached concerning the slaying of Hávar and Jodur. Thereafter, Thorgeir stayed with Bersi for a long time. Thormód and he were the best of friends. They got themselves a large boat, and seven other men joined them. They roamed about in various places, that summer, and were greatly disliked.

There was a man called Ingolf who lived in the Glacier Firth district. He was called Ingolf Sviðinn (Sulky) and the farm on which he lived, Sviðinn's Homestead. His son was called Thorbrand, a fearless man, hard to get along with, and unpopular. Both father and son were most unfair in their dealings with other men, taking possession of their goods by force or robbery. Both lived in Vermund's district, and he uniformly afforded them his protection because they always made him valuable gifts. For this reason their overbearing acts against many were not easily paid back, as Vermund's pledge[10] protected them.

Sigrfliód was the name of a woman. She was a widow and lived in the Glacier Firth district. She was a clever person, greatly liked, and had given help to many a one. The firth lay between her farm and Ingolf's, and yet she had a good deal of trouble from them.

Thorgeir and Thormód had made ready to sail north along the Strands[11] for fishing, but when they were about to leave they had contrary winds so that they were not able to get out of the firth. Many had suffered great damage at their hands, that summer. Toward the beginning of winter a favorable wind arose, so they hoisted their sail and sailed out of the Ice Firth with a gentle breeze. Their boat made little headway on that account; and when they had been sailing a while the weather began to thicken and snow to fall. And when they came to the mouth of the Glacier Firth a sharp and cold gale struck them with snow and freezing weather. Then what with the driving snow and the darkness of night they did not know where they were going. They drifted with the wind, and heavy seas broke over them so they were wet through and through and their clothes froze on their bodies. [Rán's daughters[12] tempted the youths, offering them their embraces.] They finally managed to get into a firth. They rowed into it, and at its head there was a boathouse, with a boat inside. They pulled their boat on land and secured it against the weather. Then they went up and looked for a house and found a small one. They knocked at the door and a man came out and greeted them. He asked them to come in out of the bad weather. They went into the living room. A light burned there. They seated themselves on the lower bench. The people inside welcomed them. Then a woman asked who was their leader. She was told that it was Thorgeir and Thormód and their company who had come.

"And who is asking?" they said. They were informed that it was Sigrfliód, the mistress of the house, who had asked.

"I have heard you spoken of," she said, "but have never seen you before. Have you had good weather and made good friends today?"

They answered: "Many would say that we had equal luck with both. But it depends on who is speaking."[13]

Sigrfliód answered: "I suppose you are right about that."

IV · THEY ATTACK INGOLF AND THORBRAND

THEN she ordered her servants to pull off their outer clothes.[1] A fire was kindled and their frozen garments were thawed out, then food was offered to them and they were given bedding and were well taken care of. They quickly fell asleep. The snowstorm accompanied by great cold lasted all night.

[Elri's hound[2] howled all night long with untiring jaws and gnawed all lands with the teeth of cruel cold.]

When day dawned one of the men went out to look at the weather, and when he returned Thorgeir asked what sort of weather it was outside. The reply was that it was the same as it had been the evening before.

Sigrflióð said: "You need not be concerned about the weather, because you are welcome to stay and have whatever we have to offer, and I don't want you to leave before the weather gets better."

Thorgeir answered: "That is kindly offered, lady; but it is not the storm that worries us, because we do not have to look out for wives nor children nor livestock."

The storm abated then, and a thick sheet of ice covered bays and firths. One morning Sigrflióð arose early to look out and came back in a hurry. Thorgeir asked her how the weather was.

She said: "It is fine weather outside, with clear sky and no wind."

Thormóð said: "Let us get up then, fellows!"

Sigrflióð said: "What do you intend to do?"

Thorgeir answered: "We want to go north to the Strands and try our luck there, but would like to leave our boat here."[3]

Sigrflióð said: "Strange men you are, to want to go to the Strands for whales but refuse a catch which is both nearer and more honorable."

Thormóð said: "What kind of catch might that be?"

She said: "More honorable and manly it seems to me to kill the evildoers who plunder folks here than to go for whales."

Thormóð said: "What men are you talking about?"

She said: "I mean Ingolf and Thorbrand, who have done much damage and harm to many a man. Many would be avenged if you slew them, and many would reward you nobly for it."

Thormóð said: "I am not sure whether it is a wise counsel you are giving us; because they are friends of Vermund's, and there will be consequences if any harm is done them."

She said: "Now is borne out the saying 'bad men are better heard of than seen.' You consider yourselves great heroes when cowing cottagers, but you quail when put up to a real test of manhood."

Then Thorgeir started up and said: "Stand up, men, and let us repay the lady of the house for her hospitality."

They got up and armed themselves; and when they were ready they crossed the firth on the ice and came to Ingolf's farm before the folks there had arisen. Ingolf awoke and heard men walking by the houses. There were quite a number in the company and their shoes were frozen hard. Thorgeir and his men went up to the door and knocked. At that the men who slept in the bedroom awoke and got up quickly. Ingolf and Thorbrand always slept in their clothes, because they had incurred the hostility of many men. They had two men-servants with them, and all armed themselves. Each took his spear in hand. They went to the door and opened it and saw eight men standing outside, all armed. They asked who was their leader.

Thorgeir spoke up: "If ever you have heard people talk about Thorgeir Hávarsson and Thormód Bersason, now you may see them in person."

Thorbrand answered: "To be sure we have heard of Thorgeir Hávarsson and Thormód, but rarely to their advantage. What may your business be here?"

Thorgeir answered: "It is our business here to settle a score between you and other men. We shall let you choose one of two things: either you give up all the property you have wrongfully acquired, and thus purchase your life, or else defend yourselves like men so long as your life lasts."

Thorbrand answered: "We gained our property by manhood and valor and shall not part with it otherwise than we gained it. But I am thinking, Thorgeir, that you will have your morning meal on my spear rather than on my property."

Thorgeir said: "My dreams generally come true, as they do in my whole kin; and I have dreamt a great deal about myself and but scantily about you; and everything will turn out

just as I have dreamed about you, and that is that your Lady
Hel will take you into her arms, and so you will have to part
with all your property, because as the saying goes: 'ill gotten,
ill lost.' "

V · INGOLF AND THORBRAND ARE SLAIN. SIGRFLIÓD PACIFIES VERMUND

AFTER this exchange of words, Thorgeir and Thormód
made for them but forbade their followers to attack either
son or father because they wanted to overcome them themselves. It was difficult for Thorgeir and Thormód to see
clearly indoors because it was dark in there and lighter outside; so it was easier for those inside to defend themselves
than for those outside to attack them. Ingolf's man-servants
sallied out now and then and wounded the followers of Thorgeir. But in the end Thorbrand fell by Thorgeir's hand, and
Ingolf by Thormód's. Ingolf's servants were badly wounded,
but not beyond recovery. Thormód refers to this occurrence
in his memorial poem on Thorgeir:

> 3. Death he dealt to Thorbrand—
> dauntless was the ruler-of-
> sea-trees[1]—told was't widely—
> trifling though their quarrel:
> fell before the steersman
> far-famed of mast-horses[1]—
> loss of life was great there—
> luckless the son of Ingolf.

Thorgeir and his men took two horses and loaded them
with food, and they drove away with them three of the fattest
cattle and returned the way they came across the firth. Sigrfliód was standing outside when they arrived. She welcomed
them and asked how matters had gone, and they told her.

She said: "On a good errand you left here, and skillfully
you have carved your whale and at the same time avenged

the harm and shame and dishonor of many a man. Now I shall journey to the Water Firth to find Vermund and tell him what has occurred. Meanwhile you stay here and wait till I return." They told her to do as she had planned.

Sigrflióð ordered her servants to go with her. They launched a six-oared boat which she had, and they rowed toward the upper end of the Ice Firth and did not stop till they came to the Water Firth late in the evening.

She said to her followers: "Now you are to remain close-mouthed and say nothing about what has happened, and I shall be the spokesman for us."

They said that they would do so. They went up to the farm and found people to speak to. Vermund welcomed them and asked the news, but they said they had none. They stayed there that night and were entertained well. In the morning Sigrflióð said that she wished to start on her way home. Vermund urged her to stay longer.

"You rarely visit us here, and it would be well if you did not rush off so hurriedly."

She said: "I have little chance to get away from home ordinarily, and now I would not care to miss this good traveling weather; but I would ask you to see me off, Vermund."

"Let us go then," he said.

As they were walking down to her boat Sigrflióð said: "Have you been told of the manslaughters in the Glacier Firth?"

Vermund said: "What manslaughters are you talking about?"

She replied: "Thorgeir Hávarsson and Thormóð Bersason have slain Ingolf and his son Thorbrand."

Vermund said: "They stop at nothing, these sworn-brothers, and now they are killing my men. It is only to be hoped they will not kill more of our people."

She said: "It was to be expected that you would feel that way about it. However, some would say that they did not kill these men as an unfriendly act against you but rather, that they committed these slayings for you. For who is to punish ill deeds like robbery and plundering, if you do not, you who are

called chieftain of the district? It seems to me that Thorgeir
and Thormód did what you should have done or had someone
do for you; and you would think as I do if you looked at it
the right way. For this reason I have come to visit you, because I wish to purchase forgiveness for Thorgeir and Thormód—not because I consider the men they killed worth aton-
ing, since they forfeited their lives and goods long ago, but
because I wanted to show you due honor in every way; and
here I have 300 in silver, which I want to give you to purchase
forgiveness for Thorgeir and Thormód."

And with that she took a purse from under her belt and
poured the contents into Vermund's lap. The silver was of
good weight. At that Vermund's brow lost some of its wrin-
kles and he was pacified and promised that he would forgive
Thorgeir and Thormód to some extent. But he said he did not
desire them to prolong their stay in the Ice Firth district.
With that they parted.

Sigrflióð journeyed home to her farm and told the sworn-
brothers what the outcome of her meeting with Vermund had
been. They thanked her for the advice and help she had given
them. The remainder of the winter they stayed with her, and
when spring came, and with it better weather, they launched
their boat and readied it. And when they were all set to sail
they thanked her for her hospitality and good treatment of
them and her active support in their dealings with Vermund.
They parted on most friendly terms. They sailed north to the
Strands and remained there all summer. They were successful both in their catch and in other matters, and received from
all men whatever they demanded [because everybody was
afraid of them as is the cattle of the lion when he falls upon
the herd].

Bersi removed himself to Laugaból in Laugadale, since
Vermund did not desire the refuge of Thorgeir and Thormód
to be so near to his own dwelling. In the fall the two journeyed south from the Strands to the Ice Firth and there drew
their ship on land where it seemed convenient to them and
stowed everything away for the winter. Then Thormód went
to stay with his father, but Thorgeir wanted to go south to

Reykianess to his kinsfolk. And their companions each went
to his own homestead. On parting they agreed to meet again
in spring where their ship was laid up, and that all would then
return to the Strands for fishing and whaling. Thus they
parted good friends.

VI · THORGEIR SLAYS BUTRALDI

THORKEL was the name of a man who lived in Gervidale.
He was well-to-do, not much of a fighter but rather of a for-
bearing disposition and timid in his heart. He was married,
and there were only three people in the house, with a hired
woman as the third.

There was a man called Butraldi. He was a bachelor, without house or home, a fellow of great size and strength, ugly,
pugnacious—a man who had committed many murders, hot-
headed and vengeful. He hired out in summer time in various
places, and in winter he roamed about, with two other men,
and took up his abode with some farmer or other for several
days in a stretch. He was distantly related to Vermund in the
Water Firth, and so he did not get paid back quickly what he
deserved.

This Butraldi, then, with two other men came to Thorkel's
homestead in Gervidale some time in the evening; and though
Thorkel disliked to part with his food he did not dare to refuse to give them shelter. So they were shown in and a light
made for them. They sat there with their weapons about
them, while the other persons of the household were in the
front part[1] of the house.

Some snow had fallen on the mountains and drifted, but in
the countryside the ground was altogether bare, and the
creeks were swollen although the weather was freezing, and
it snowed a bit. Thorkel came into the room where the men
were sitting and asked some questions about things he wanted
to know. Among other things he asked Butraldi which way
he was going to take, and he answered that they were headed

south across the Broad Firth. Thorkel was not sure if the weather would permit their crossing the heath[2] on the morrow. He did not like their staying there, but his courage failed him, [for his heart housed both shabbiness and cowardice].

Right then he heard a knocking at the door, which did not make him feel any better. He went to unlock it and saw a tall man standing outside, all armed. Thorkel asked the man his name, and he said it was Thorgeir. He asked whose son he was and was told, the son of Hávar. Then he quaked with fear, and his heart sank within him.

He said: "A man by the name of Butraldi is staying here with two other men, and I don't know how you will get along with him. I believe he will have something against you, because he is a friend of Vermund, your enemy. But I can't stand the sight of blood and would faint if you two fought together."

Thorgeir said: "No harm will come to you through my presence here, farmer."

And so he went in, and Thorkel and his wife brought a table and set it in front of Butraldi.

"Meager is the fare I offer," he said, "so come here, Thorgeir, and sit by Butraldi."

Thorgeir crossed the room and sat down by Butraldi at the side of the table. We are told exactly what fare they had: two platters were set before them, and on one was an old piece of meat from the short ribs, and on the other a huge piece of an old cheese. Butraldi said a brief blessing and took hold of the short ribs. He cut pieces off it and ate, and did not stop before all the meat was off the bones. Thorgeir seized the cheese and cut off as much as he wanted. It was hard and difficult to cut. Neither of the two would share with the other either the food or the knife. But though the fare was poor they did not add to it from their own provisions because each thought that would show him to be soft. Food was also set before Thorkel and his wife as they sat before the fire; and every now and then they came into the room where the men sat, opening the door warily and looking in.

When the guests had had their fill Thorkel and his wife came in, and she took the food from the table.

Then Thorkel said: "I would like you two to repay me for my entertainment by not fighting with one another while you are in my house, because it would give me a great deal of difficulty if you did that while you are here. It seems best to me for Thorgeir to sleep with us in the bedroom and that Butraldi and his men should sleep here in the sitting room."

And so they did, and slept during the night. But when morning dawned Butraldi and Thorkel rose up early, and so did Thorgeir. A light was made in the living room and the table was brought out and food set on it the same way as before. This time, Thorgeir got hold of the short ribs and cut pieces off for himself, and Butraldi got busy with the cheese. And when they had enough Butraldi and his men left and went up the valley along the beaten path. A little later, Thorgeir left too and also went up the valley.

A creek flows down this valley, and a steep ridge of the heath leads up from Gervidale to the highroad. On this ridge there was a big patch of hard-frozen snow at that time. Thorgeir observed the way Butraldi and his men went and was sure they were going to have a hard time climbing up by way of the hard-crusted snow. So he crossed the creek and climbed up on the other side of the valley while the others were climbing the ridge, and then rejoined the path. Meanwhile Butraldi had arrived at the snow patch and made his way up by cutting steps in it with his axe. Thorgeir was able to watch Butraldi because he had gained the height.

Butraldi then shouted: "See how the hero ran away from us."

Thorgeir replied: "I did not run away from you. I went the other way so as not to have to cut steps in the ice. But now I am not going to run away from you fellows."

Thorgeir was standing at the very brink of the slope while Butraldi was still cutting steps in the snow. But when he had got about midway up Thorgeir sat down on his spear shaft with the point forward and the axe on his shoulder, and slid down the snow patch toward Butraldi. He heard Thorgeir whizzing down and looked up. But before he knew it Thorgeir struck him full on the breast with his axe so that it penetrated to the vitals and he fell backward. Thorgeir lept over him, scattering Butraldi's men as he rushed down to level ground. About this exploit[3] the following verse was composed by Thormód:

> 4. Well behooves it, warrior's-
> work[4] to praise—the raven
> sated oft forsook it—:
> silent lies Butraldi;
> though little thanks, methinks, did
> therefor people give the
> sword's-bold-swinger for that
> slaying—I'll not deny it.

Butraldi's men did not dare to avenge him and attack Thorgeir, because they did not wish to find night quarters under his weapons.[5] So they thronged about Butraldi while Thorgeir turned back to climb the heights and traveled till he came south to Reykiahólar. He found a hospitable reception and stayed there that winter well cared for. It was a hard winter over all the land. Cattle died and conditions were difficult. Many men went north to the Strands to provide themselves with whale-meat.

VII · THE FIGHT OVER THE WHALE. THORGEIR AND THORMÓD PART COMPANY

THE spring after, Thorgeir went to the Ice Firth to where their ship was laid up. He was joined by Thormód and their crew, and they sailed north to the Strands[1] as soon as they had a favorable breeze. Thorgils Mársson was the name of a man who lived at Lækiamót in the Wood Dale. He was big and strong, skillful in the use of arms, and a good farmer. He

was related to Ásmund hærulang, Grettir's father, and also
to Thorstein Kuggason. He also had gone to the Strands with
his crew and had begun to cut up a whale which had drifted
on the common lands there.

Thorgeir had had no luck in catching anything where he
had gone, neither whales nor anything else. Then he learned
that Thorgils was flensing a whale at another spot. So he and
Thormód went to that place, and when they got there Thorgeir said: "You have done a good job, cutting up this whale,
and now it would be fair to let others besides yourselves have
a chance to take advantage of this good thing; because all
have equal rights here."

Thorgils answered: "Well spoken! Let each keep what he
has cut off."

Thorgeir said: "You have sliced a big piece from the
whale, and you are welcome to what you have already cut off.
But now we wish you would do one of two things, either
leave the whale now and keep what you have cut off, so we
can take what is left of him, or else go halves with us on what
you have cut off and what is still left."

Thorgils answered: "I haven't the least desire to leave the
whale, nor do we propose to part with what we have cut off
him, at least as long as we can hold on to him."

Thorgeir said: "In that case we shall see how long you can
hold on to the whale against us."

Thorgils answered: "Well and good, we shall see about
that."

Then both parties armed themselves and made ready for
the fight. And when they were ready Thorgeir said: "It were
best, Thorgils, that we two fought with one another, for you
are full-grown, hardy, and tested in battle, and I am eager to
fight it out with you. Let no one else have a part in our fight."

Thorgils said: "So be it."

Their parties were about equal in strength. So they attacked and fought each other. Thorgeir and Thorgils exchanged blow for blow, for both were skilled in arms; but
because Thorgeir was destined to shed the blood of more
men, Thorgils fell by his hand. In that fray three were slain

of Thorgils' party and the same number of Thorgeir's. After the battle, Thorgils' men went north back to their own homes with heavy hearts. But Thorgeir took possession of the whole whale, both cut and uncut.

On account of the slaying of Thorgils, Thorgeir was condemned to outlawry, and Thorstein Kuggason and Ásmund hærulang saw to its execution.[2]

Both Thorgeir and Thormód remained that summer along the Strands. All men feared them [and they overtopped them all like noxious weeds in a field]. It is said that once when they were at the height of their insolence, Thorgeir said to Thormód: "Do you know of other two men equal to us in keenness and manhood, and equally tested in many deeds of valor?"

Thormód replied: "Men could surely be found who are no less brave than we."

Then Thorgeir said: "And which of us would overcome the other if we two fought together?"

Thormód answered: "That I don't know; but I do know that this question of yours will put an end to our comradeship and fellowship and that we can no longer get along together."

Thorgeir said: "I had not thought at all of trying to see who was the better man of us two."

Thormód replied: "You were surely thinking of it while you spoke, and this will part our fellowship."

And that was the outcome. Thorgeir got the ship, and Thormód, the larger part of the property. He went to Laugaból, but Thorgeir remained along the Strands during the summer and was the source of great trouble to many a man. In the fall he drew his ship on land for the winter and stored his goods. Then he went to Reykiahólar and stayed with Thorgils that winter. In his *drápa* on Thorgeir, Thormód alludes to their disagreement in the following stanza:

> 5. Folk have heard how fain our
>   foes had been—with hate they
>   slander sowed—to part the
>   sailor from his brother:

I care but to recall the
comradeship betwixt us—
good it was, though grudged us
guileful men our friendship.[3]

VIII · BIARNI APPROPRIATES THORGEIR'S HORSE AND IS SLAIN BY HIM. THORGEIR SAILS TO NORWAY AND JOINS KING ÓLAF'S BODYGUARD

A SHIP was laid up ashore in the North River, near Flói—ships used to run in there frequently. On this ship, Thorgils and his brother Illugi secretly bought a passage for Thorgeir and had wares brought aboard corresponding in value to Thorgeir's share in the ship. Neither Thorgils nor Illugi rode to the beginning of the Assembly,[1] that summer, for the reason that they did not care to cross the valley courses of the Broad Firth before Thorstein Kuggason had left the district to ride to the Assembly; because they had in mind to accompany Thorgeir to his ship, and Thorstein had been instrumental in procuring Thorgeir's outlawry.

There was a man called Skúf who lived in Hundadale, one of the valleys of the district of The Dales. He was a good husbandman and of a helpful disposition. His son, Biarni, lived with him. Skúm was the name of their sheepherder. Now people journeyed to the Assembly, but Thorgils and Illugi, together with Thorgeir, rode east from Reykiahól. They had sent men ahead to the Assembly to have their booths put in order. Illugi and his men ate their evening meal in the Saurbœr farm and continued eastward during the night, intending to eat breakfast in Hundadale. At break of day they arrived in Middale before entering the Thickets. There they ate and slept. Thorgeir had a red horse, large and beautiful, excellent for riding. In the course of the morning they called on their men to fetch the horses, and they got up to look for them. But Thorgeir's horse was to be found nowhere. They were a long time looking for it, because all the slopes around them were covered with great thickets. However, the horse was not to be found. So they took the load off a pack horse and divided it among several horses, and gave Thorgeir that horse to ride.

Then they caught sight of a man on a good riding horse of red color. He was driving some sheep in front of him up the gravel banks from the direction of Saudafell. He was driving them fast because he rode a fine animal. To Thorgeir that horse looked very much like his own. He pretended not to notice, but kept a sharp lookout which way the man was headed. He saw that he drove the sheep toward the farm in Hundadale.

Skúf had received some ewes from Laxdale in the west, in payment for some debt, and they had run away; so his son Biarni had gone to look for them and had got hold of Thorgeir's horse. About that time Illugi and his men rode up to the farm in Hundadale. The brothers told their men to take the packs off their horses outside the farm and not to let them graze on the home meadow. But they themselves with a few men rode up to the farmhouse.

Thorgeir rode to the sheepfold where he thought he recognized his horse. Skúm had just got home and was driving the sheep into the fold, and Biarni was sitting on the horse after driving the ewes he had found into the fold.

Thorgeir asked: "Who is the man there on horseback?"

"His name is Biarni."

Thorgeir said: "You have a beautiful horse there—who owns it?"

Biarni answered: "It is certainly beautiful, but who owns it I don't know."

Thorgeir said: "Why did you take the horse?"

Biarni said: "Because I thought it better to ride than to walk."

Thorgeir said: "I think it would be best now for you to get down and return the horse to its owner."

Biarni said: "I will not have far to ride now as I shall not have to go farther than the house door."

Thorgeir said: "I shall ask you to get down at once."

Biarni replied: "It will not hurt the horse if I ride it up to the house."

Thorgeir said: "I shall advise you not to ride any further now."

Biarni was about to turn the horse toward the yard gate and ride up to the house, when Thorgeir thrust at him with his spear and at once ran him through so that he fell off the horse dead. Skúm the shepherd saw him fall and ran out of the gate of the fold he was about to close. He seized his axe and hewed at Thorgeir with both hands. Thorgeir warded the blow off with his spear, and with his right hand he drove his axe into Skúm's head and split it down to his shoulders so that he died at once.

The men who were with Thorgeir now ran to the farm house and told the chieftains what had happened. It seemed to them very bad news indeed. They got some men to lead Thorgeir away at once, so that he would not come into the sight of the father of the slain man or any of their kinsmen. Then they told Skúf what had happened. He saw that under the circumstances he could do no better than have the right to award himself damages, which the brothers offered him to make up for the slayings, also considering the standing of the men who offered it, and especially since the slayer had already been outlawed.[2] So the case was settled in that fashion. Thormód refers to these slayings in his *drápa* on Thorgeir:

> 6. For his angry ill-will—
> ice-cold steel did clash there:
> raw flesh got the raven—
> wrathfully slew he Már's son.
> Still was the stem-horses'-
> steerer[3] at the slaying—
> eager for the onset
> ever—of Skúm and Biarni.

Thorgils and Illugi ate their morning meal in Hundadale. Then they rode south to the Borgar Firth and accompanied

Thorgeir to his ship. A man called Gaut had come aboard it, the son of Sleita. He was a near relative of Thorgils Mársson, whom Thorgeir had killed. Gaut was a large man of great strength, quarrelsome and aggressive. He had arranged with the skipper for his passage and had no idea that Thorgeir intended to leave the country on the same boat. He knit his brows as soon as he saw Thorgeir, and the men thought it might be rather dangerous business to have two men aboard with such dispositions as both of them had.

The ship was all ready for sailing, the lading had been stowed away, and the wares belonging to Gaut covered in the hold. Now when Thorgeir overheard the mutterings of the Norwegians about having both Gaut and him aboard, he said: "I don't mind in the least sailing with Gaut, however much he may knit his brows about it."

But whatever Thorgeir said about getting along with Gaut, it was decided to break bulk and put Gaut's wares back on land; whereupon he rode away north into the country.

The Norwegians then sailed down the river and out to Seleyrar (the Seal Flats). Illugi and his brother did not ride away from the district before the ship was on the high seas. Then they rode to the Assembly with a numerous following and came to terms, in behalf of Thorgeir, for his slaying of Thorgils Mársson, and brought about his acquittal.[4]

Thorgeir and his shipmates were tossed about at sea for some time, but finally they saw land forward, and the Norwegians knew it to be Ireland. A peaceful reception for them seemed unlikely if they drifted to land there.

Thorgeir said: "It is more than likely that if we defend ourselves stoutly we shall sound the death knell for some of them before we ourselves are killed, and that will prove as good a defence as any."

So they dropped anchor in the offing and fetched out their weapons and prepared for battle, in case that was offered. They saw a great multitude of men on land and a forest of spears. But though the Irish had long-shafted spears they did not reach to them. So their lives and goods were in no danger, and they sailed away as soon as the wind was favorable.[5]

They made England and stayed there for a while; and as Thormód says in his *drápa*, Thorgeir received fine gifts from chieftains there. Then he sailed to Denmark and was accorded well-nigh royal honor by the Danes, as Thormód relates in his poem.[6]

Thereupon he sailed to Norway to pay his respects to King Ólaf the Saint. He presented himself to the king with courtly greeting, and the king took it in good part and asked him who he was.

He answered: "I am an Icelander, and, my name is Thorgeir."

The king spoke: "Are you Thorgeir Hávarsson?"

He answered: "That is who I am."

The king said: "I have heard your name mentioned. You are tall of stature and appear to be a man of great prowess, but you don't seem to have luck with you."

The king invited Thorgeir to remain at the court, and he became one of the king's bodyguard. The king made much of Thorgeir because he proved himself in all dangers to be an unusually brave man and great-hearted, too. He went on a trading journey south to the land of the Wends,[7] where at that time there was little personal security for merchants from the north. This journey brought him fame, because he managed to get what he wanted from everyone. Thereafter Thorgeir arranged it so that he always spent one winter in Norway with King Ólaf, and the next in Iceland, at Reykiahólar. He would then sail his ship into the Borgar Firth and thence to Flói, up the Northrá River.[8] There he would lay up his ship on the western bank. That place is now called Thorgeir's Shed, and is south of the ridge called Smithy Ridge. Six times Thorgeir sailed his ship from Iceland, according to Thormód:

> 7. Six times did the sea-steed's[9]
>   sailor—ever was the
>   wound-snake's-wielder[10] free of his
>   wealth—set out from Iceland.

Oft he sailed his surf-steed[11]
swart-tarred[12]—have I heard that—
foemen feared he little—
from his homeland seaward.

IX · THORMÓD FALLS IN LOVE WITH THORDÍS. HE IS WOUNDED BY KOLBAK

IT BEHOOVES us now to tell about what Thormód was doing while Thorgeir was abroad on his expeditions. After parting with Thorgeir he went to live with his father Bersi at Laugaból and spent many a winter there. He always found it very dull at home because there was little company.

A certain woman called Gríma lived on a farm called In the Bight.[1] She was a widow and well-to-do. People said that she was skilled in many things, in fact, was a sorceress. [And because at that time the Christian faith was still young and weak it seemed to many a matter of importance if a person was skilled in witchcraft.] Gríma's daughter, Thordís, was a handsome and showy woman, very clever with her hands. She lived with her mother. Kolbak was the name of Gríma's slave. He was big and strong and of an attractive appearance, and a good fighter, too. Thormód used to come frequently to this place and to sit and talk long hours with Thordís—so much so that people began to hint that he was seducing her.

When Gríma heard these rumors she took occasion to speak to Thormód and said: "A good many people are saying that you are seducing my daughter Thordís, and I don't like it at all that her reputation is besmirched by you. It isn't that you would not be a good match for her, but rather because the men who might have a mind to ask for her hand would hesitate to do so if they heard that you had intentions that way; for they stand in awe of you. Now if you want to marry her I shall give you my consent."

Thormód replied: "You have spoken to the point about this business, and I shall heed your words; but I have no mind to marry. But if I had I could not do better than marry your daughter. However, there cannot be any question about that."

And with that they parted.

Thormód went home and remained there for the rest of that summer. But when winter came all water courses froze over tight and traveling was easy. Also the lake at Bight was frozen over. Time hung heavy on Thormód's hands because there was little diversion at Laugaból. So he renewed his visits to Thordís; and again there came up the same trouble and rumors about their friendship as before. Thormód always had his sword and shield with him when he went to Bight, because there was some trouble outstanding between him and certain men. Gríma talked to Thormód again and asked him to discontinue his visits, "so as to keep scandal from my daughter." Thormód gave her a soft answer but kept coming as before.

One day when Thormód was again in Bight Gríma said to Kolbak: "I want to send you to a farm with weft needed for a cloth that is being woven there."

Kolbak made ready to go, and Gríma unlocked a chest she had, and out of it she took some balls of yarn[2] and also a large old cutlass, sharp and keen.

She handed it to Kolbak and said: "Take that along so you will not go unarmed."

Kolbak seized it. Then she put the hanks of yarn inside his cloak. She stroked over his entire body with her hands and over his clothes too. Then Kolbak went his way.

The weather began to thicken and there came a thaw that removed what snow had fallen. As the day was waning Thordís said to Thormód: "I wish you would go home another way than you usually take. Go around the inlets of the Bight and then take the upper way to Laugaból."

Thormód answered: "Why do you wish me to go that way?"

Thordís said: "Maybe the ice in the firth has become rotten, with this thaw, and I don't want anything to happen to you."

Thormód replied: "The ice will hold all right."

Thordís said: "I won't ask you again, and I shall feel badly if you won't do what I ask you to."

As Thormód saw that she attached great importance to what she asked of him, he promised to take the way she wanted him to go.

Late in the evening he left the Bight; but when he had gone a short way it occurred to him that after all it could not make a great difference to Thordís which way he took. So he changed his mind and took the short cut across the bay on the ice. There was a sheep pen on the inner corner of the bay, with a hedged plot around it. Thormód started to pass the gate of the pen when out ran a man from the shed with sword brandished. He slashed quickly at Thormód and gave him an ugly wound on the arm above the elbow. Thormód threw his shield down and, drawing his sword with his left hand, he grasped it with both hands and let blow follow blow in quick succession. But they took no effect on Kolbak, because he was so shielded by Gríma's spells that no weapon would harm him. Kolbak hewed at him only that once.

He said: "You are altogether in my power now, Thormód —I can do with you what I will; but I won't do any more to you."

With that Kolbak turned to go home, and there he told Gríma what had happened. She thought that he had spared Thormód too much. And she did not let it be known that she had set a trap for Thormód.

Thormód tore his linen trousers and bandaged his wound. Then he went home to Laugaból. A serving woman was waiting there for him in the sitting room with a light. All the others had gone to bed. She set a table before him with food, but Thormód hardly touched it. The servant woman noticed that he was bleeding and went in to Bersi to tell him that Thormód had returned and that his clothes were all covered with blood. Bersi got up and went to the living room. He greeted Thormód and asked what had happened. Thormód told him about his encounter with Kolbak and the wound he had received.

Bersi said: "Do you mean to say that he was invulnerable to your sword?"

Thormód answered: "Again and again I slashed at him, and he was wounded no more than if I had hit him with a piece of whalebone."

Bersi said: "That proves Gríma's sorcery."

Thormód then spoke a verse:

> 8. Off I warded, warrior—
>   wounded was I, though, by
>   shining steel—my shield then
>   shed I—mighty sword-blow.
>   Vain 'tis to avenge the
>   villain's treacherous onset,
>   fain though would I, fire-of-
>   flood's-dispenser,[3] do so.

Bersi said: "So it is; I don't know when this infamous deed can be avenged, because we shall have to deal with witchcraft."

X · BERSI VAINLY SEEKS KOLBAK. GRÍMA HELPS KOLBAK LEAVE ICELAND

BERSI then bandaged Thormód's wound, for he was a good healer. On the morning following, Bersi went to the Bight with a number of men. But before he arrived Gríma said to her men-servants: "You are to go to the living room and sit on the lower bench[1] and stay there while Bersi and his men are here."

They did as she told them and sat there with their weapons. Gríma seated Kolbak right in their midst and passed her hands over his head. Soon Bersi and his men arrived at the farm and knocked at the door. Gríma went to open it and greeted them.

Bersi said: "I am thinking you are mighty little concerned about our health.[2] But you might as well know that we wish you all ill."

Gríma said: "I am much surprised at what you say. I had thought you were our friend as we are yours. What has happened?"

Bersi said: "Only what you are well aware of."

Gríma said: "We have not heard of anything happening recently. What might it be?"

Bersi said: "Then I must tell you about the wound your slave, Kolbak, inflicted on Thormód, my son."

Gríma said: "This is bad news and heinous, if it is indeed so. Because I sent Kolbak to a farm with yarn, and he did not return last night. I suspect he does not dare to face me, because he knew what fast friends Thormód and I are. I have long thought that Kolbak might be hand in glove with Thordís. And now he has been fool enough to attack Thormód in his jealousy—so fine a man—and to bring disgrace on my daughter and get me into shame and trouble. I shall have to call him to account for this, so far as I can."

Bersi said: "Some people think, Gríma, that you are not above playing a double game once in a while; but we shall soon see whether there is any truth in what you say."

Gríma replied: "I would only be too glad and pleased if you would search the farm and so remove the suspicion from me that I had been partner to Kolbak's misdeed."

Then Bersi went into the room with his men, seating himself on the seat of honor. He sat there for a while, not seeing Kolbak although he was seated right opposite to him, because Gríma with her sorcery had made him invisible. Then Bersi went through the whole farm and could not find Kolbak. Thereupon he formally named Kolbak as the perpetrator of the attack on Thormód and then returned home. Thormód's wound grew worse, and he was laid up for a long time. He was left-handed thereafter for the remainder of his life.

Kolbak remained in hiding with Gríma during the winter. The spring after, they had the law on Kolbak, and in that Assembly he was condemned to outlawry. A ship was moored at Vadil. Its skipper was a Norwegian called Ingolf. It was all clear for sailing when the Althing met, but there was no favorable breeze.

As soon as the people of the district had left to attend the Assembly Gríma spoke to Kolbak and said: "I fully expect that you will be declared outlaw on account of the wound you gave Thormód. But because this happened on my account I shall set you at liberty and you shall no longer be a slave. Also, you are to make ready four horses in secret—two for riding, and two for carrying the loads of wares and provisions which I shall give you. I shall see you to a ship, if that can be managed, and procure you passage at Vadil."

Kolbak was much pleased with his release from slavery and the other gifts from Gríma. He managed to depart stealthily with her at night from the Bight so that no one became aware of it. They rode over the Gláma Plateau to the Arnar Firth and thence over the mountains to Barda Strands.

When they arrived that night at Vadil the merchants were asleep on their ship, and the skipper himself ashore in his tent on land. Gríma unfastened its edges while Kolbak tended the horses. Then she entered Ingolf's tent, for she had made his acquaintance before, and awakened him. Ingolf greeted her and asked her the news.

Then Gríma said: "My business in coming here is to procure passage for a man who has come with me."

Ingolf replied: "Who is the man?"

Gríma said: "His name is Kolbak."

Ingolf answered: "Is he the man who attacked Bersi's son, Thormód?"

Gríma said: "Yes, he is."

Ingolf replied: "A risky thing, to take along a man who is likely to be declared an outlaw this summer; especially when men so determined as Thormód and Bersi have the case in hand. Also, we have been lying here all clear for sailing for a long time. So it is possible that Bersi may return to the district before we shall be able to sail, and then we might not be able to hide the man from him."

When Gríma saw how reluctant Ingolf was to do what she wanted she fetched out a purse from under her cloak and from it poured two hundred silver coins into his lap and said: "This money I shall give you for helping to get Kolbak away."

Ingolf said: "This is good money, but dearly bought if Thormód and Bersi come upon us before we can get away with a man on board who is outlawed by them."

Then Gríma said: "How about this arrangement? You have Kolbak along and take the money I have offered you and help him get away—providing you get a favorable breeze today."

Ingolf replied: "Very well, so let it be."

So he accepted the money and got up and conducted Kolbak out to the ship with his wares. Meanwhile Gríma busied herself up on land. She recalled to her mind the olden magic songs she had learned in her childhood, and soon the counterwind stopped which had prevailed so long. Ingolf hastened to pack his sleeping bags and go on board; and by early morning everything was shipshape. When the sun stood in the southeast a fair wind had sprung up. Ingolf and Kolbak went on land to say farewell to Gríma. She made ready to go and got herself someone to ride with her, and nothing is told of her journey before she came home to Bight; and that was a long time before people returned from the Assembly. But Ingolf boarded his ship as soon as Gríma had left. They spread sail with favorable winds and had a quick journey. When they arrived in Norway, Kolbak joined a company of vikings and proved himself a bold fellow in all dangers.

Thormód returned from the Assembly to Laugaból and stayed with his father for several years. It is not reported that Thormód got any further redress for his wound than the outlawry of Kolbak.

XI · THORMÓD COMPOSES THE COAL-BROW DITTIES

IT ALWAYS had seemed boring to Thormód to stay on his father's farm. After the Assembly in summer he made ready to bring in the dried fish which Bersi had out in Bulungar Inlet.[1] They sailed in a large boat that belonged to Bersi and had a favorable breeze in the Ice Firth; but when they arrived at the opening of the Arnar Dale a counterwind struck them so that they were driven from their course. They dropped anchor and left the boat to put up their tent on land, and they were forced to stay there some time, because there was no chance for them to sail away very soon.

A woman lived in the Arnar Dale called Katla. She was the widow of a man called Glúm. Their daughter Thorbiorg lived at home with her mother. She was a well-bred woman, though not particularly beautiful, with black hair and eyebrows, wherefor she was called Coal-Brow. Her face had an intelligent expression and good color. She had shapely limbs and was slender and of average height. She toed out a little when she walked.

It so happened one day that Thormód left his tent and went up to the farmhouse. When he entered the living room there were only womenfolk inside. Katla greeted him and asked who he was. He named himself. Then she asked whose son he was, and he told her that too.

Katla said: "I have heard about you but haven't seen you before."

Thormód remained there during the day, and the women enjoyed his company very much. He let his eyes roam over to the daughter of the house, and he thought her beautiful. She also cast looks on him and began to like him. He remained there the day over, then returned to his tent in the evening. Thereafter, Thormód visited day after day at Katla's house. Now and then love ditties came over his lips, and the women of the house were pleased to hear them.

One day Katla said: "Tell me, Thormód, have you any

business here in the inlet as you are traveling with your father's servants?"

Thormód answered: "I have no other business than to have a good time, because I find it dull at home."

"Would you consider it more entertaining to go with them or to stay here while they fetch the dried fish, and to have a good time here? Because you are welcome to stay here if you wish, for we enjoy your company."

Thormód answered: "It is kind of you to say that, and I shall accept your invitation, because I do indeed enjoy being here."

Thereupon Thormód went back to his crew and told them that he wished to stay behind while they went to bring the fish from Bulungar Inlet, and he told them to call at Arnar Dale on their return trip so that he could go back with them. With that they parted, and Thormód returned to the farm while they left as soon as the wind was favorable.

Thormód remained half a month in Arnar Dale. During that time he composed verses in praise of Thorbiorg Coal-Brow which he called Coal-Brow Ditties; and when he had finished them he recited them in the hearing of many.

Katla drew a large and valuable ring from her finger and said: "This ring I give you, Thormód, as a reward for the poem and with the name I bestow on you; because from now on you shall be called Kolbrúnarskald—poet of Coal-Brow."

Thormód thanked Katla for her gift, and he was ever after known by the name she had given him.

Bersi's men now returned and called for Thormód, and he went aboard with them. He thanked Katla for the hospitality she had shown him, and Katla said that he must not pass her place by if ever he came that way again. And so they parted. Thormód returned to Laugarból and remained there the rest of the summer.

But when winter came and the ice on the bays held, Thormód recalled his friendship with Thordís, the daughter of Grima in Bight. So he made his way to Bight again. Grima welcomed him with every sign of joy, but Thordís showed her pique and sulked, as women are apt to do when they are put out with a man. Thormód was not slow in noticing that and observing that she looked askance at him and also otherwise showed her displeasure. It occurred to him that it might be wiser to meet her half-way. So he reminded her of their former friendship.

Thordís said: "I have heard that you have got you a new sweetheart and that you made a poem in praise of her."

Thormód said: "Who is this sweetheart you are talking about that I'm supposed to have praised in a poem?"

Thordís said: "It is Thorbiorg in Arnar Dale."

Thormód said: "I deny that I composed the poem about her. What is true is that I composed a poem praising you, when I was in Arnar Dale, because I became aware of how much you surpassed Thorbiorg in beauty and breeding; and I came here to recite the poem to you."

Then Thormód recited the Coal-Brow Ditties, changing those passages to express the praises of Thordís which most definitely had been meant to be in praise of Thorbiorg. And this poem he dedicated to Thordís to reconcile her with him. [And just as dark fog arises out of the sea and then passes away again, leaving bright sunshine and pleasant weather, likewise did the poem dispel dark animosity and gloom from the mind of Thordís and made the light of her warm love turn to Thormód again.] Now Thormód came often to the Bight and was well received.

When some time had passed it happened one night when Thormód was at home in Laugarból that he dreamed that Thorbiorg Coal-Brow appeared to him and asked whether he was awake or asleep. He said he was awake.

She said: "You are asleep, but that which seems to befall you now will surely come to pass when you wake. How about it? Have you given another woman the poem you composed in praise of me?"

Thormód said: "That is not true."

Thorbiorg said: "Indeed it is. You have given the song of praise you made about me to Thordís, the daughter of Gríma, and you have changed those words which most clearly showed that it was meant for me; because, coward that you are, you did not dare to say the truth for whom the poem was intended. And now I am going to repay you for your lying and deceit: you will feel such a pain in your eyes that they will seem to pop out of your head, unless you confess to all the world that this is my poem and stick to that."

And it appeared to Thormód in his dream that she was in a great rage, and he thought he caught a glimpse of her as she disappeared.

He awaked with such pains in his eyes that he could hardly stand it without screaming, and could not sleep the rest of the night. He kept to his bed in the morning. And when all were up and dressed Bersi wondered why Thormód was lying abed so long and asked him if he was sick. Thormód answered that he had a pain in his eyes.

Bersi said: "Ill is indeed whose eyes do smart." Then Thormód spoke this verse:

> 9. Ill indeed did I, when
> all of Coal-Brow's Ditties—
> me dreamed I got my guerdon—
> I gave to the Thrúd-of-brooches:[2]
> with pain as punishment—her
> pardon had I rather—:
> smote my eyes the sage one
> savagely. I rue it!

Bersi asked: "What was your dream?" Thormód told him his dream and how he came to compose the poem.

Bersi said: "Baneful sweethearts have you; from the one you receive a lasting wound from which you barely recovered, and now from the other the threat that you will lose both your eyes. My advice is that you turn back your poem to what it was in the beginning."

Thereafter Thormód made known to everybody just what the case was and before many witnesses returned the poem to Thorbiorg as it was in the beginning. Then the pain in his eyes left Thormód and he was entirely well again.

XII · THORGEIR SLAYS SNORRI

Now we must tell of Thorgeir, Hávar's son, King Ólaf's
man. One summer he sailed his ship into the White River and
from there up into the North River. He passed the winter at
Reykiahólar with his kinsmen and there sold his wares. But
early in spring he journeyed south to the Borgar Firth and
prepared his ship for sailing. Then, a little while before the
meeting of the Assembly, he rode back west to Reykiahólar
to fetch the wares he had traded in for those he had brought
out. These he moved to the Wood Strands and procured himself horses and rode back to the Borgar Firth, together with
one other man who rode ahead, leading another horse. Thorgeir himself rode last, driving several pack-horses before
him. He had his shield on his back and was armed with helmet, spear, and battle-axe.

A certain man lived at Hvítastadir called Snorri and nicknamed Hœkils-Snorri.[1] He was a big and strong man, well-
grown but grim in countenance. He was much disliked because of his hot-headedness and vengeful disposition. His son
was named Helgi and still a boy at this time. The houses of
this farm formerly stood further down on the tongue of land
than now. It was called Mel. A large shed for lambs used to
stand on the west side of the home meadow at a place now
called Snorri's Homestead.

Past this place, then, rode Thorgeir and his man. And
while the latter was rounding the farm the pack-horses
which Thorgeir drove before him ran away into the home
meadow. Snorri came out of his house just as Thorgeir was
chasing the horses to get them out of the home meadow. But
the pasturage was good there, so that one horse stopped in it
while he was chasing the other. Snorri went back into the
house and got himself a big spear with barbs and then went
at the horses, cursing them and Thorgeir, and hitting and
wounding them with his spear. Thorgeir was afraid he might
kill them. So he leaped off his horse, and with shield and
battle-axe in his left hand and the spear in his right he at-

tacked Snorri. The latter defended himself wi
backed up to the lamb shed. Two of Snorri
had seen him grab his spear and run out in
took his axe in hand to help Snorri. Thorg
off with great dexterity [and then attacke
strength and fearlessness of a lion]. They were
soon because their axes had short hafts and Thorgeir thrust
at them hard and often. So Snorri and his men retired into
the lamb shed. Its doors were low and narrow, so that it was
difficult for Thorgeir to get at them there. So he leaped upon
the roof and began to rip it up; but Snorri thrust at him with
his spear as soon as he had made a hole, and Thorgeir was
slightly wounded by him. He laid his spear aside and took
his axe in his right hand. Snorri thrust at him furiously
through the hole, but Thorgeir fought him off with shield
and battle-axe and tried to lop off Snorri's spear from its
shaft, and he finally succeeded in doing so. In the same moment Thorgeir jumped down into the shed through the hole
and split Snorri's head with a blow of his axe so that he fell
down dead. Then Thorgeir turned to Snorri's men and attacked them nimbly, protecting himself with his shield, and
leveled blows at them with that axe of his which was wont to
give many a man his last night's rest. It ended with his slaying both of them.

Thereupon he left the shed and mounted his horse. He rode
to the door of the farmhouse and there found people to speak
to. He told them that Hœkils-Snorri wished to speak with
them and would wait for them in the lamb shed.[2] Then he
rode away and rejoined his companion. He had driven the
pack-horses out of the home meadow while they fought. Both
then rode to the ship. Thorgeir made all ready on it and sailed
to the Seal Flats. There he waited for a favorable wind, and
when it came he put out to sea. He had a good passage, with
favorable winds, and made Norway. There he went immediately to the court of King Ólaf and was received well by him.
Concerning these events Thormód speaks in his drápa on
Thorgeir in this stanza:

10. Wrathfully ripped up Snorri's
    roof, battling, he who on
    Hœkil's son for his horses'
    harm did wreak his vengeance:
    stirred to stronger wrath then—
    striven have I to utter
    true words—Thorgeir there was
    three men's death together.

Snorri's son Helgi lived for a long time at Hvítastadir. He was unlike his father and other kinsmen, both in looks and disposition. He moved the farm to where it is now. He was called Helgi the White, nor was that nickname given to him in contempt[3] but because he was a handsome man with beautiful hair of light blond color. It is after him that the farm was called Hvítastadir. Helgi was well-liked and a good husbandman, helpful to the people in the district. He had a fight with Thorstein, the son of Egil, about the low-lying meadows along the Gufá River. Thorstein had wanted to buy them, but Helgi refused to part with them. One day, Helgi went to these meadows with his men-servants and carried the hay south across the lowlands with his oxen, as had been his wont. Thorstein came upon them at the Long Islands, south of Hvítastadir. There Thorstein and Helgi fought together, and Helgi was seriously wounded. But friends of both parties who knew how matters stood between them came and separated them. Peace was concluded between them on the condition that Thorstein was allowed to buy the meadows against making recompense to Helgi for his wounds according to the judgment of well-meaning men.

XIII · THORGEIR SLAYS THÓRIR. VEGLÁG'S THEFTS. THORGEIR JOINS THE ORKNEY EARL

THÓRIR was the name of a man who lived at Hrófá in the Steingrims Firth—a very self-assertive man, and very overbearing and disliked. He had quarreled with a follower of King Ólaf at a fair in the Steingrims Firth and wounded the man severely. No amends had been made by him for it, and when the king heard of it he was greatly displeased. He called Thorgeir Hávarsson to him and said: "It is my desire, Thorgeir, that you avenge the act of violence committed against my follower in Iceland and thus teach Icelanders not to assault my followers."

Thorgeir answered: "I live in hopes that I may avenge the offence which was committed against you by this deed."

The king said: "I have summoned you in this business because I believe that you are the man to carry out my wishes."

Thorgeir answered: "It is my bounden duty to do as you command."

Thereupon Thorgeir made ready his ship to sail for Iceland early in summer. He had favorable winds and made land at Vadil. From there he journeyed to Reykiahólar and began to erect a hall.[1] A man called Veglág helped Thorgeir in building the house, each on his own side. It had inside planking[2] the whole length of the house, and this same planking was still in good condition when the second Bishop Magnus[3] was consecrated in Skálaholt.

Toward the beginning of winter Thorgeir rode north to the Hrófá River in the Steingrims Firth. With him was Veglág the builder. They came to the farm late in the evening and knocked at the door. A woman answered their knock. She greeted them and asked who they were. Thorgeir told her and asked whether farmer Thórir was at home. She said that he was.

Thorgeir said: "Ask him to come out."

She went in again and told Thórir that two men were standing outside "who want to speak with you."

He said: "Who are these men?"

She answered: "I am thinking that the one is Thorgeir Hávarsson."

Thórir got up and took his spear. He went to the door, setting the point of his spear on the threshold, and greeted them. Thorgeir did not return his greeting.

He said: "My business here is to find out what restitution you will make to King Ólaf for the outrage you committed against his follower."

Thórir said: "Are you the rightful prosecutor in the case?"

Thorgeir answered: "I am indeed, because I have the king's charge in the matter."

Thórir said: "It may be that you have his charge, but I don't seem to hear the king's words though I hear you speaking."

Thorgeir answered: "It is true enough that you do not hear him speaking, yet maybe you will get to feel his power."

And when he least suspected it, Thorgeir thrust at him with his spear. It went deep into his breast so he fell down dead within the doorway. Very soon after, Thorgeir and his companion left the place, and we hear nothing about their journey till they returned to Reykiahólar. About this occurrence Thormód composed this stanza:

11. Well I mind the mere-ship's
master, how with his spear he,
carrying out the king's wish,
killed the son of Thórir.
Thus avenged the warlike
wealth-destroyer[4] the wounds of
Odd—were the eagles sated;
all went as the king wished.

That winter many thefts were committed at Reykiahólar. Many possessions disappeared from out of people's chests, and things came to such a pass that nearly everybody lost something, however strong a lock they had on their chests, and yet no lock was found broken. Illugi Arason was home at Reykiahólar that winter.

Now after Yuletide the two brothers gathered all the members of their household, and Thorgils said: "It is known to you all that this winter there have been many thefts and that much has been stolen, though kept under lock and key. We shall now make a search, beginning with us two brothers, then Thorgeir, and after that we shall look into the chests of the other members of the household. And if the stolen goods are not found here we shall go to other farms and search there."

This was done and the chests of all were searched, but the stolen goods were not found. The builder Veglág owned a large chest which had not yet been looked into. Thorgils told Veglág to open that chest and let people see what was in it.

He replied: "I have never before been searched like a thief, and I am not going to open my chest."

Thorgils said: "You are not the only one to whom this is done. Our own chests have been gone through, and you are no exception."

Then Veglág replied: "Even though you all have been searched I shall not open my chest for you to go through it."

Then Illugi started up and, shouldering a hatchet, went at the chest and said: "Here I have a master key which undoes all chests and locks, and with it I shall open your chest if you don't hand me the key."

Veglág saw that Illugi would break up his chest unless he undid it himself, and handed him the key. Then Illugi unlocked the chest and found there many keys which fitted all the locks in Reykiahólar. He also found in it many things which people had missed. So it was clear to all that Veglág was the thief. He was forced to confess, then, and to acknowledge his thefts and had to show them where he had hidden things in various places outside the house.

Then Illugi said: "It seems to me that Veglág has forfeited his life,[5] and it is my advice that he be hanged."

Thorgeir said: "You surely don't mean to dispose of your own servant in such fashion."

Illugi answered: "It would seem unwarranted to me to let such an arch-thief escape with his life."

Then Thorgeir said: "Whatever may seem right to you, you will find the life of the man dearly bought if I have anything to say in the matter."

Illugi said: "You show great zeal to save the life of this

thief; but you will have little advantage from him, and not always will your intercession save him even though he escape with his life this once. Let him be off now and never show himself again on Reykianess."

Thorgeir said: "So let it be."

Then Thorgeir accompanied Veglág westward[6] to Laugaból in Laugadale, where Bersi and Thormód lived, and called upon them to house Veglág till early summer, "and then bring him to my ship at Vadil," when Thorgeir would see to get him out of Iceland. They took Veglág in that winter because of Thormód's friendship with Thorgeir;[7] and in spring they brought him to Thorgeir's ship, and he took him along. Their ship made land in the Orkney Islands.

At that time, Earl Rognvald, the son of Brúsi,[8] was making ready for an expedition against the numerous vikings infesting the islands who robbed both merchants and farmers. He intended to punish them for their ill deeds. Thorgeir sold his ship and joined the company of Rognvald. But Veglág went up into Scotland. There he committed many thefts and finally was put to death. Rognvald held Thorgeir and his companions in high esteem, because the greater the tests to which he was put the greater a hero he proved himself to be. As Thormód says in his *drápa*:

> 12. Came on board the keel-steed's[9]
>   keen-eyed rider, dauntless
>   when with Rognvald he would
>   harry: eke that tell we;
>   little spared he landmen's
>   life in combat bloody:
>   did deeds of derring-do the
>   dreadless son of Hávar.

On this expedition Thorgeir acquired fame as a courageous and skillful fighter in all situations requiring gallantry. And the earl, too, acquired fame in this expedition because he was victorious wherever he fought that summer, and he brought security to merchants and farmers.

XIV · THORGEIR'S LAST STAY WITH KING ÓLAF

LATER on in the fall Thorgeir sailed to Norway and stayed at the court of King Ólaf the following winter, where he enjoyed great honor. King Ólaf thanked him for what he had done to avenge the affront Thórir had done him. Illugi Arason also was at the king's court that winter. In the spring Illugi made ready to sail to Iceland. Thorgeir said to Illugi that he would like to sail with him, but Illugi answered him as follows: "It seems ill advised to me that you come out to Iceland. You have committed deeds of violence in many districts so that you will not be safe in most places there, whereas here you are greatly honored by the king and are getting along well with everybody. I do not care to take you from a place where you enjoy peace to one where every man's hand is against you. Because you will not receive so much honor in all Iceland as you receive here from the king every day."

"It may be," said Thorgeir, "that I shall manage to get to Iceland even though you are not willing to grant me passage."

Thereupon Illugi got his ship ready for sailing and left as soon as he had a favorable wind. And when Illugi was out on the high seas Thorgeir one day went before the king and asked for permission to depart.

King Ólaf said: "It would seem to me that you are less in favor in Iceland than here with us. I believe it would be better for you to be here than in Iceland, just because you fare better here."

But Thorgeir was so insistent in his entreaties that the king said: "Now it will come to pass as I predicted the first time you came to our court: that you would not prove to be a fortunate man in all respects. Now I shall give you leave to go to Iceland; but it is not likely that we shall see each other again if we part now."

Thorgeir answered: "I give you thanks for allowing me to depart, but it is my intention to rejoin your court next summer."

The king said: "It may well be that you intend to do that, but it is not likely to happen."[1] After this conversation they parted.

Thorgeir engaged passage with a Norwegian called Jokul and sailed to Iceland with him. The ship made land at Vadil, and Thorgeir went to stay at Reykiahólar. Illugi was tossed about a long time that summer, but late in the fall he landed at Hraun Haven on Melrakka Plain, and there he drew his ship ashore for the winter and set men to guard it. Then he journeyed south[2] across the country to get home to Reykiahólar. Gaut Sleituson, whom we have mentioned before, went to meet Illugi when he was about to set out from the north and engaged passage with him for the following summer.

One day when Illugi and his men were resting and feeding their horses at the Mid Firth a man came riding up to the pasture. He wore a white cloak. He greeted Illugi, who returned his greeting and asked who he was.

He said: "My name is Helgi."

Illugi said: "Where do your kinsfolk live and where is your home?"

Helgi answered: "My kinsfolk live widely scattered, but most of them here in the north; but I am at home nowhere; nor am I fortunate enough to stay a whole year in one place, but I always hire myself out in summertime. And so I did this summer, and many people know me when they hear my nickname."

Illugi asked: "And what is that?"

Helgi said: "I am called Helgi Seal's Stone."[3]

Illugi said: "That is a rare nickname, but I have heard you mentioned."

Helgi said: "My business here is to ask if you will give me passage on your ship next summer."

Illugi said: "Are you in trouble? And have you any property?"

He replied: "No, I am not in any trouble, and I have no property at all. Still you might find me useful, because I am a very handy man."

Illugi said: "Have you any particular skill?"

He replied: "I have no particular skill, but I put great trust in my legs, and I have a sound chest, too, so that no one can overtake me."

Illugi said: "That is a good thing for those easily frightened."

Helgi said: "I won't say that I take fright easily; but I should like to know if you will take me along on your ship."

Illugi said: "Come to me next spring and help me transport my wares, and then I shall let you sail with me."

"That suits me very well," said Helgi.

Then they parted, and Illugi rode west to Reykiahólar and remained there during the winter.

XV · THE FOSTER-BROTHERS EYÓLF AND THORGEIR SPENDTHRIFT. THORGEIR HÁVARSSON SLAYS GAUT

Two BROTHERS lived in Garpsdale, one called Kálf and the other, Steinólf. They were young men, well-to-do and well-liked. A certain woman lived in Ólafsdale, by the name of Thordís. She was a widow, thrifty and a good housekeeper. Her son Eyólf lived with her at her place, an efficient and well-thought-of man. Thorgeir was the name of a kinsman of Thordís whom she had brought up as a foster-child. He was a brisk fellow and nicknamed Thorgeir Spendthrift, because he always bought more than he needed, as soon as he had some money in hand. From early childhood the two foster-brothers, Eyólf and Thorgeir, had been close friends. Both were brisk, energetic men who always got along well with one another. But an old servant woman of Thordís often showed her disapproval of them and their tussles together. But they made game of her, and the more so as the old woman grew vexed with them.

One day when they were wrestling in the hall they kept returning to the spot where she sat and tangled up her handiwork underfoot.

Then the old woman said: "It is little credit to you to ruin my work and to make sport of me; but let me tell you something: however great friends you two are now, a time will come when your friendship will end in the worst way possible."

They said: "That is a mighty unpleasant prediction you are making us."

The old woman said: "Whatever you may think about it, all will come to pass as I foretold you."

The spring after the winter which Illugi and Thorgeir had passed together at Reykiahólar, Thorgeir asked Illugi to grant him passage across the Iceland Sea, and Illugi agreed to that. Kálf and Steinólf from Garpsdale also were to sail with Illugi. Toward spring, about the time they were getting ready for the journey, Illugi said to Thorgeir: "I shall ask you, kinsman, to ride north[1] to the ship with my men and to get it ready for sailing during the time the Assembly meets. I myself have business at the Assembly and wish to meet my friends there; and from there I mean to ride north and I wish that all may be shipshape when I get there."

Thorgeir said that it should be as he desired. So he repaired to the ship which was laid up at the Melrakka Plain while Illugi rode to the Assembly. Steinólf, Kálf, and Helgi Seal's Stone all went with Thorgeir. Their wares had been sent ahead. But Thorgils Arason and his sons Illugi and Ari, together with a company of men, rode from the Broad Firth to the Assembly.

When Thorgeir arrived at the harbor in the north he launched the ship and got everything ready. Gaut, the son of Sleita, had also come to sail with them, but he had a different set of messmates. Firewood was scarce at that place, and the two companies went out in turn to collect it, now Thorgeir and his messmates, now Gaut and his.

One day it happened that Thorgeir went out to collect wood and Gaut stayed behind. The messmates of Gaut had their kettle over the fire, and when it began to boil there was no more firewood. They told Gaut about their difficulty. Then Gaut went to Thorgeir's tent, took down his spear and chopped off the head, throwing it on his bed and taking the shaft along. He also took Thorgeir's shield with him to the fireplace. There he split both shield and spearshaft and fed the fire with it so that the food could get done.

Thorgeir returned toward evening and immediately missed his weapons. He asked who of the men had taken "both my shield and my spear."

Gaut said: "I took your shield and spear and split them to feed our fire, otherwise we could not have cooked our food because there was no more firewood, and we did not care to eat our food raw."

Thorgeir did not let on that he was ruffled by what Gaut had done. On the next day Gaut and his companions went out to fetch firewood, and Thorgeir remained behind and worked on getting the ship ready. His messmates had too little firewood when they were about to prepare their food, and they told Thorgeir. He went to Gaut's tent and took his shield and spear and chopped up both for firewood. That provided enough to boil their food. Gaut returned in the evening and asked what had become of his shield and spear.

Thorgeir made answer: "Your shield and your spearshaft I broke up today to feed our fire because the cooks were out of firewood."

Gaut said: "You are everlastingly provoking us."

Thorgeir answered: "As you sowed so shall you reap."[2] Then Gaut struck at Thorgeir, but he parried the blow with his axe and so made it glance off, but was slightly wounded on his foot. Then some men ran between them and pinned them fast.

Thorgeir said: "No need to hold me, because I shall not lift my hand against him now."

So they broke away and went each to their tent. Then they ate their supper and lay down to sleep. And when the men had fallen asleep Thorgeir arose and took his axe in hand. He went to Gaut's tent, lifted up the tent flaps, went in to where Gaut lay and waked him. Gaut woke and started up and wanted to seize his weapons, but at the same moment Thorgeir struck at him and cleft his head down to his shoulders.

Then Thorgeir went back to his own tent. Gaut's tentmates woke at the commotion and crowded about Gaut's body and made ready to bury him. About this occurrence Thormód composed this stanza:

13. Quickly after their quarrel—
     quarter was not given—
     Gaut, old Sleita's son, he
     slew, famous in battle:
     punished with painful wounds, he
     paid—oft cometh great re-
     ward to him that ventures—
     with his life in combat.

XVI · THORGRÍM AND THÓRARIN PLAN TO OVERCOME THORGEIR HÁVARSSON

AFTER this occurrence Thorgeir one day saw a ship sailing into the harbor from the high seas, and it cast anchor at some distance from Thorgeir's ship. He rowed to that merchant vessel with his men and asked who was the master of it. He was told that its skippers were Thorgrím Einarsson, nicknamed the Troll, a man from Greenland, and Thórarin, nicknamed Arrogance,[1] the son of Thorvald, from the northern quarter. They in their turn asked who was the master of the ship which lay at anchor there. They were told that Illugi Arason owned the ship but that Thorgeir Hávarsson was in command at the time. Thorgeir asked them how many men they had aboard, and they told him they had a crew of forty. So Thorgeir saw that the odds were much against him, in case of hostilities, since his crew numbered only twenty ablebodied men.

Thorgeir said: "This is what I ask of you skippers: Many men say that both of us are of a fairly overbearing disposition and apt to be aggressive. Now I would ask of you that

we do not let our valor and hardihood become foolhardiness
and quarrelsomeness. It would seem advisable to me that we
make a truce between us as a precaution."

Thorgrím and Thórarin agreed to that, and a truce was
made between them, as Thormód declares:

> 14. Then did Thorgeir pray those
> thanes gold-ring dispending,
> grith to give him, seeing
> greater were their numbers.
> True-hearted trusted he the
> troth they pledged him, fully;
> when that, the while, in their
> hearts they did betray him.

And when this truce was concluded between them, Thorgeir returned to his ship. He had all the wares of his shipmates brought on board and anchored his ship at some distance from the land. Then all his crew remained aboard
because he did not altogether trust Thorgrím and Thórarin
even though the truce had been concluded between them.

Now some people from the countryside came to Thorgrím's ship and related the slaying of Gaut Sleituson which
had taken place there in the harbor and which Thorgeir had
not mentioned to him. And no sooner did Thórarin hear
about it than he spoke to Thorgrím alone and said: "I would
not have entered into a truce with Thorgeir had I known
about the slaying of my kinsman Gaut. Now I would like to
know whether I can expect help from you in case I wish to
avenge him."

Thorgrím answered: "I shall not fail you in this business;
but Thorgeir is likely to prove hard to deal with."

Thórarin said: "Someday let us take our fine clothes and
linen and other valuable outfit and spread them out on shore
for drying. Then very likely some of Thorgeir's men will
come to admire the goods and we can kill them first and so
reduce their numbers."

Thorgrím said: "You may try that if you wish."

Now, Thorgrím and Thórarin owned both ship and lading

together and had had the intention to sail to Greenland and
had therefore not removed their wares to the land. One day
when the weather was fine, Thórarin and his crew brought
the precious garments, linen, and other costly wares on shore,
and spread them out to dry. On the same day Kálf and Steinólf and ten other men rowed to the land to fetch water; and
when they saw the goods spread out on shore three men of
their crew ran to see them. As soon as they got there they
were killed. After that, Thórarin and Thorgrím with their
troop attacked Kálf and his men. Kálf and Steinólf were
seized and fettered, the other six men were killed by the
water's edge. Helgi Seal's Stone gave one of Thórarin's men
a mortal blow at the beginning of the skirmish and then took
to his heels. They pursued him but could not catch him. He
made his way over the mountains and ran day and night and
did not stop till he arrived at the Assembly. There he told
Thorgils and Illugi what had happened in Hraun Harbor
when he escaped.

XVII · THORGEIR HÁVARSSON'S FALL

AFTER the events just told, Thorgrím and his crew seized
the boat in which Kálf and his men had rowed to land, and
with it returned to their ship, Thorgeir was on board his ship
with eight of his men, and they were unaware of what had
happened on the shore because a hill rose between the ship
and the place where they fetched their water. They were altogether taken aback when they saw Thórarin and his crew
approach in their ship and two boats filled with battle-clad
men. Thorgeir and his men seized their arms and defended
themselves well. Thorgrím moved his ship close alongside
that of Thorgeir, and a sharp fight started at once. Very soon
they boarded Thorgeir's ship and fought their way with hard
blows. Thorgeir wielded his axe with both hands, and for a

long time no one could touch him, because no one was anxious for night quarters under his battle-axe, and yet many of them got just that. Thorgeir's men soon were overcome. Then he himself leaped back to the prow and defended himself there, because the odds against him were great. As Thormód said in his *drápa*:

> 15. Stand most stiff was made on
>   stem-horse[1]—heart of oak was
>   shown—'gainst forty foemen
>   fighting—by the ring-breaker,[2]
>   on his boat ere, battling
>   boldly—he wounded many—
>   fending him eke fiercely,
>   fell nathless the warrior.

> 16. Well then showed the shower-of-
>   shafts-urger[2] all dauntless
>   how to help his fellows,
>   hazardous though the fighting.
>   That I heard, how Thorgeir
>   thewful showed him—was that
>   tiding told us; aye will
>   treasure-dealer[2] famed be.

All praised his valor who had seen how manfully he fought, and all men thought that there had never been found his equal. [He rained hard blows with undaunted courage and strong arms, and his own stout heart served him as shield and coat of mail. A stand such as he made had never been seen before. It was the Almighty who had laid so bold and fearless a heart into Thorgeir's breast, nor was such valor of human origin but stemmed rather from the Creator of All.] And because Thorgrím's men found it a greater test of their manhood to come to close quarters with Thorgeir than to fondle their women, they did not find it so easy to overcome him. In fact, his fall was dearly bought. For, as Thormód tells us, Thorgeir slew fourteen men before he fell. Two whom he killed are mentioned in the *drápa* on Thorgeir. Már was the name of the Norwegian who wounded him in the arm, whereupon he gave Már a fatal blow. Another Norwegian, named Thórir, ran his spear through him, but Thorgeir closed with him, with the spear in his body, and slew him. About these deeds, Thormód composed the following stanzas:

17. Never, heard I, harbored
    Hávar's son the thought of
    giving in to the greedy-
    gull-of-combat-feeders:[3]
    Már and Thórir the men whom,
    matchless in speech, Thorgeir—
    grith was not given nor
    gotten, heard I—slew there.

18. Dauntless, the hero death did
    deal to thirteen foemen
    on ship ere laid low was,
    lifeless, the mere-steed's ruler.
    Done now have I herewith:
    heed give to my story—
    winsome flow my words—of
    warrior's feats of slaughter.

But even after Thórir had fallen and his spear still was in Thorgeir's body, he yet stood up, and there was a bitter fight, because now Thórarin and Thorgrím were close by and set upon him, and then Thorgeir fell and died. Thórarin Arrogance cut off his head and brought it away with him. Some say that they cleft open his breast to see what sort of heart he had, with such courage as his; and they say that it was small. [For some think that the hearts of courageous men are smaller than those of cowards. They say that there is less blood in a small than a big heart and that much blood in the heart makes a man afraid. They say that a man's heart fails him because his heart's blood takes fright and so also his heart.]

XVIII · THORMÓD BECOMES KING ÓLAF'S MAN

AFTER this battle Thórarin and Thorgrím dissolved their partnership, because Thórarin thought he had won a great victory and would have great honor in Iceland on account of it. In dividing the common property Thorgrím received the ship, and Thórarin, the movable property. Thorgrím sailed to Greenland and had a successful journey. Thórarin procured horses and men and with eleven others left the harbor to ride south. He carried Thorgeir's head with him in a bag by the saddle-straps as a token of his great victory. It was their custom to take the head out of its bag when they stopped for rest and to put it on a mound and make sport with it. But when they came to the Island Firth, a short way from the farm Naust, to graze their horses, and took the head and set it on a mound as they were wont, the head looked frightful to them with its eyes open and the tongue hanging out of the mouth. They were gripped with fear at the sight, so they dug a hole beside it with their axes and thrust the head into it and covered it over with turf.[1]

The people of the Melrakka Plain unloaded Thorgeir's ship and brought to land and buried there the bodies of all the men who had fallen on the ship and on land, for they did not care to take the bodies to a church, because at that time there was no church anywhere near the harbor. After the battle Kálf and Steinólf were unfettered and helped the people of the Melrakka Plain bury the dead. They guarded the wares which had been on board the ship until Illugi arrived. [For though Christendom still was young in Iceland at the time, yet it was not considered right to appropriate the goods of men who had been slain.][2]

Illugi sailed from the Melrakka Plain to Norway that summer; but Thormód the Poet of Coal-Brow sorrowed long after Thorgeir's fall and sailed from Vadil to Norway the same summer. And from the mouth of the Grímsá River, Eyólf from Ólaf's Dale and Thorgeir Spendthrift sailed, and made land on one of the Lofoten Islands in Norway. As soon as he landed, Thormód the Poet of Coal-Brow went to the court of King Ólaf the Saint.[3] He greeted the king, and the king received him graciously and asked who he was and who were his kinsmen.

Thormód said: "I am an Icelander. My name is Thormód, and Bersi is the name of my father."

The king said: "Are you the man called the Poet of Coal-Brow and the sworn-brother of Thorgeir Hávarsson?"

"Yes, indeed," answered Thormód, "I am the man."

The king said: "You shall be welcome here on his account. I want you to know that I am aggrieved at the slaying of Thorgeir my follower, and shall owe gratitude to him who avenges him."

Then Thormód spoke this stanza:

> 19. Bold must be who long doth
> bide, king—though thou speakest
> winsome words to every
> one—in thy dread presence:
> kinsmen few in king's court—
> cowards none, sire—have I—
> more is on my mind as
> my task—loyal to thee.

The king said: "Your skaldship promises to be enjoyable." Then Thormód joined the body-guard of King Ólaf.

That summer a ship arrived from Greenland. Its skipper was a man called Skúf. His kinsfolk lived in Greenland, and he was an experienced sailor and merchant, intelligent and well-liked. He had the ear of King Ólaf and belonged to his company. Skúf journeyed to the king's court and stayed there during the winter. That same winter there were in Norway Illugi Arason, Steinólf and Kálf, Eyólf and Thorgeir Spendthrift. In the following spring, half a year after Thorgeir Hávarsson was slain, Thorgils Arason and his son Ari preferred suit against Thórarin and the other men involved in the slaying. They followed up the matter with great energy, in view of the outrage which had been committed. The parties came to an agreement about the matter at the Assembly, and Thorgils fixed two hundred ounces of silver as the amount to

be paid altogether. They were to be paid at the Assembly, and
Gudmund the Powerful was to receive one hundred, accord-
ing to Thorgils' decree.[4] In the course of the same summer
Thórarin was slain at a gathering in the Island Firth.

That same summer Kálf and Steinólf returned to Iceland.
They made land at Vadil on the Barda Strands and rode
home to their farm in Garpsdale. Eyólf and Thorgeir Spendthrift bought a ship in Norway and when they had readied it
they also sailed to Iceland. They were tossed about for a long
time but finally, late in fall, came to the Borgar Firth. There
they had a disagreement where to land. Eyólf wanted to sail
to the Straum Firth because the wind blew in that direction,
but Thorgeir Spendthrift wanted to let the ship drift and try
whether the breeze would carry them around the glacier,[5] and
then steer toward Dogurdarness. So they went to the mast,[6]
and the question was put to the men, how many wanted to sail
on and how many were for drifting with the wind. But because the men were weary of the sea most of them preferred
to sail toward land. The two foster-brothers were so enraged
at each other that they seized their weapons; but the men prevented them from fighting. The ship made land in the Straum
Firth; and as soon as it was made fast, Thorgeir Spendthrift
procured himself a horse and rode west to Garpsdale. There
he arranged to stay with the brothers, Steinólf and Kálf.
Eyólf remained by the ship till it was laid up for the winter.
Then he journeyed home to his mother in Ólafsdale and
stayed with her during the winter.

XIX · EYÓLF AND THORGEIR
SPENDTHRIFT KILL ONE ANOTHER

THE soothsaying woman we mentioned before fell sick
during the winter. She lay abed for a long time and finally
died the night after Palm Sunday. Her body was brought by
boat to Reykianess because there was no church nearer to
Ólafsdale than Reykiahólar. Eyólf and his men took the body

to the church there. And when it had been buried the weather worsened, snow fell heavily, and it grew so cold that the firth froze over and it became impossible to sail back to Ólaf's Dale.

Then Thorgils said to Eyólf: "It would seem wise for you not to start home before the end of Easter Week. I shall then furnish you men to accompany you home if the ice permits; but if the boat cannot get through I shall equip you with horses to ride home. However, if it is necessary for your men-servants to return to your farm, then let them ride ahead."

Eyólf said: "I shall gladly accept your offer."

Then Eyólf's men-servants rode home, rounding the Króks Firth, but Eyólf remained at Hólar till toward the end of Easter week. On the fifth day he told Thorgils that he wished to depart, and Thorgils said that it should be as he wished. He had a horse newly shod for him and offered him a man to accompany him if he so required. But he said he preferred to ride alone. He took the way inland from Reykianess, rounding the Beru Firth and the Króks Firth. When he had but a little way to ride to Garpsdale the two brothers, Kálf and Steinólf, were standing outside by the wall of their house talking together. They thought they saw a number of men walking over the meadow from the direction of the sea, and they seemed to recognize Thorgeir Hávarsson and the nine men who were slain on the ship together with him. They were all covered with blood. They walked toward the farm house and then out of the enclosure again, and when they came to the brook which flows through the farm they vanished. The brothers were aghast at this vision and went back into the house.

Onund was the name of the cowherd in Garpsdale. He came out of the stable just as the brothers had gone in. He saw a man riding over the meadow from seaward, mounted on a handsome horse. He was girt with a sword and had a spear in his hand and a helmet on his head. When he came near the farm the cowherd recognized him as Eyólf. Onund went into the living room. Only a few people were there—Thorgeir Spendthrift and some women.

Onund raised his voice and said: "Right now Eyólf is riding by the farm." No sooner did Thorgeir hear that than he ran out with a spear in his hand. At that time Eyólf rode over the home meadow. Thorgeir ran after him, but Eyólf rode on, unaware that someone was running after him. When he came to the Garpsdale Creek he found it full of floating ice and looked for a place to cross it. Thorgeir called out to him to wait if he dared. When Eyólf heard his voice and saw Thorgeir pursuing him he jumped down from his horse and ran to meet him, and in the encounter they pierced each other with their spears and both fell at the same time. Thus was fulfilled what the old wise-woman had prophesied them.

When the two brothers, Kálf and Steinólf, had recovered from the faintness into which their vision had thrown them they asked: "Where is Thorgeir?"

And they were told that he had taken his spear and left the house as soon as the cowherd Onund had told them that Eyólf was riding past. The two brothers rushed out of the house and through the farm down to the creek. By that time both Thorgeir and Eyólf had fallen, but were still alive. Kálf and Steinólf sat with them until they were dead. Then they took the bodies to the church (at Reykiahólar).

XX · THORMÓD AND GEST SAIL FOR GREENLAND

WHEN Thormód the Poet of Coal-Brow had been with King Ólaf one winter Skúf readied his ship for departure to Greenland. Then Thormód approached the king and said: "I would, sir King, that you give me leave to sail to Greenland this summer with Skúf."

The king said: "What errand have you in Greenland? Is it perhaps that you intend to avenge your sworn-brother Thorgeir?"

Thormód answered: "I do not know what luck I shall have in accomplishing that."

The king said: "I shall not forbid your going, for I think I know what you have in mind."

And with that they parted.

Thormód engaged passage with Skúf, and when they were ready to sail they went to the king and thanked him for all the favors he had shown them. The king wished them a good journey and in parting gave Thormód a gold ring and a sword.

When they were boarding their ship a man stepped on to the gangplank. He wore a hood coming far down so that one could not see his face. He was tall, broad-shouldered, and strongly made. He greeted Skúf, who returned the greeting and asked who he was. He said his name was Gest.

Skúf said: "And where do your kinsfolk live?"

Gest said: "My kinsfolk live widely spread. My business with you is to know whether you will give me passage to Greenland this summer?"

Skúf said: "I don't know you. Besides, I must find out if my men agree to take you along."

Gest said: "I thought it was the skipper's job to dispose of his ship, and not the crew's. For that matter, you can depend on me for performing the tasks you assign me in such fashion that your crew will not have to do them for me."

The upshot of their talk was that Skúf engaged to take him along. Gest went back into the town and returned after a while with a pack so great and heavy that two men could scarcely have lifted it. Gest found himself a place behind the lading. He had little commerce with the other men and did not meddle with what did not concern him.

Then Skúf set sail. Great waves broke over the ship, and the weather became stormy. Gest proved himself the handier the more was required of him. To some it seemed that he had the strength of two in all he did. But Thormód and he fell out about everything that happened. It so chanced that the two had to bale water together. In those days they baled ships with buckets, and not yet with pumps. Thormód was stationed below in the bilge, filling the buckets, and Gest took hold of them on the thwarts and emptied them overboard.

Thormód was not a strong man and often did not reach the pails up high enough. Gest kept saying that he should reach them up higher. Thormód made no answer but did as before. Then all of a sudden Gest let a bucket full of sea water drop on him so that he became wet all over. Thormód jumped out of the bilge and seized his weapons, and so did Gest, and they were about to fight it out. But Skúf said: "It is not right for men to fall out in a merchant ship on the high seas. Great misfortune may come of it, and something bad is apt to happen to a ship if the crew fight with one another. Now I shall ask both of you to keep the peace while you are on board the ship on the high seas."

They did so.

The ship was tossed about by strong gales for a long time. In one storm their sail-yard broke in two so the sail fell overboard. The men grabbed it and hauled it in, and in doing this, Gest showed great strength and energy. Skúf knew that those of the crew whom he had brought out of Greenland had little skill, whereas he had seen both Thormód and Gest whittle and shape many a thing from wood. So he said to Thormód: "Would you undertake to fix our sail-yard?"

Thormód said: "I am not skilled in such matters. Speak to Gest that he should do it. He is so strong that he can join both ends of the sail-yard."[1]

So Skúf went to Gest and asked him to repair it.

He answered: "I am not handy in such matters. Speak to Thormód and tell him to do it: he is so clever with words that he can join the ends together so they will hold.[2] But because we are in a bad way I shall shape one end if Thormód shapes the other."

Then each was handed his axe and shaped his end. Gest occasionally looked at Thormód over his shoulder. As soon as Thormód had smoothed his end of the sail-yard he sat down on the lading; but Gest took a little longer with his part. And when both were finished he put the ends together and they fitted perfectly. Then he spliced them, and they hitched the sail to it and sailed on.

Late in fall they made Greenland and anchored in the Ei-

riks Firth.[3] Thorkel Leifsson[4] was head of that district then.
Thorkel was a great chieftain, powerful and well-liked. He
was a great friend of King Ólaf the Saint. He quickly
boarded the ship when it had made fast and bought from the
skipper and the crew all he needed.[5] Skúf informed Thorkel
that there was a follower of King Ólaf on board named Thormód, and that Thormód was sent to him by the king for support and help if such were needed. Because of Skúf's words,
Thormód was accommodated at Brattahlíd.

Skúf himself owned a farm on Stockness in the Eiriks
Firth, opposite to Brattahlíd. With him lived a man called
Biarni. He was wise and well-liked, clever at many things,
and efficient. He managed their farm when Skúf was on
journeys. They owned it together and prospered. Thormód,
as we have said, stayed at Brattahlíd during the winter. Gest
found lodgings in the Einars Firth at the farm called Vík. It
belonged to a man called Thorgrím.

XXI · THORMÓD QUARRELS WITH LODIN

THORGRÍM EINARSSON, nicknamed the Troll, lived on
Longness in the Einars Firth. He had the authority of a
goði[1] and was a great chieftain. He was powerful and had a
great following. He was a man of unusually resolute character. With him lived his sister, Thordís, who was the widow
of a man called Hámund. Her four sons lived there too. One
of them was called Bodvar, another, Falgeir, the third, Thorkel, and the fourth, Thórd. They all were courageous and
brisk men. Thorgrím had another sister called Thórunn. She
also lived in the Einars Firth, on the farm which is called
Longness. She had a son, Liót, a man of great stature. All of
Thorgrím's kinsmen were of a blustering disposition and
very highhanded. Sigríd was the name of a woman who lived
on a farm called Cliff, and her son Sigurd lived with her. He

was a capable man, well-liked and not very self-assertive, but his character was not considered altogether stable.

There was a slave on the farm at Brattahlíd called Lodin, a good worker. His bed fellow was a woman called Sigríd. She was detailed to take care of Thormód. There was a small, detached house at Brattahlíd, at some little distance from the other buildings, in which Thorkel and his followers used to sleep. A light burned in it every night. All the other people slept in the dwelling house. Now it seemed to Lodin that Sigríd took to staying rather long in that house in the evenings and that she cared less for him than before. He bethought himself of the saying, made about loose women:[2]

> On whirling wheel   their hearts were shaped,
>   and fickle and fitful their minds.

He told Sigríd that he did not care to have her stay so long evenings in that house, and she answered him as she saw fit. One evening when Thorkel and Thormód were starting to go to this house, and Sigríd with them, Lodin seized hold of Sigríd, but she tried to wrench herself loose. But when Thormód saw that, he caught Sigríd by the hand and tried to pull her out of Lodin's grasp; but that was not done so easily.

Thorkel watched their tussle and said to Lodin: "Let Sigríd go her way; nothing dishonorable will happen to her when she attends to us in the evenings. I shall watch over her to see that no harm is done to her or to you. But it is your business to watch over her at other times."

XXII · THORMÓD SLAYS LODIN

WHEN the Yuletide festival was approaching Thorkel had the home ale brewed in order to celebrate the feast in his house and thus show his wealth; for such festivals were rarely held in Greenland. Thorkel invited his friends to celebrate with him, so that there was a numerous company. Skúf from Stockness and Biarni were also invited, and they furnished hangings, mugs, and garments for the celebration. Then they feasted during Yuletide with much glee and merriment.

On the last day, when the company was ready to depart, Lodin fetched the men their swords, clothes, and gloves which had been entrusted to his safekeeping. He also got out the boat for Skúf and Biarni, and the house servants carried their drinking vessels and garments from the house down to the boats. Lodin himself was dressed in a sealskin jacket and sealskin trousers. When he and three other men entered the house only Thormód and Biarni were inside. Thormód was lying on the bench which stood in front of the raised dais.[1] Now when Lodin and the other men entered the room Lodin caught hold of Thormód's legs and pulled him down on the floor and dragged him toward the door. Biarni jumped up, seized Lodin by the middle, and lifted him up for a hard fall. He cursed the men who kept dragging Thormód and told them to let go of him. They did so.

Thormód stood up and said to Biarni: "Stunts like that, we Icelanders don't mind at all because we are used to them in our skin-games."[2]

They all left the house and acted as though nothing had occurred.

When Skúf and his company were all ready for leaving, Thorkel went down to the boat, together with his followers, to see them off. They had a large boat, and a gangplank went up on land from it. Biarni stood by the boat, waiting for Skúf, and was talking with Thorkel. Lodin had finished handing the men their equipment and stood close by the boat. Thormód was not far from him. And all of a sudden Thormód snatched his battle-axe from under his cloak and dealt Lodin a blow on the head so that he fell down dead.

Thorkel heard the crash. He turned and saw Lodin fall. He called to his men, bidding them kill Thormód. But they hesitated. Biarni called out to Thormód to get into the boat, and he did so, followed by Biarni and Skúf. And as soon as they were on board they drew in the gangplank. Thorkel urged his men on to attack them, and wanted to fight Skúf and Biarni if they did not surrender Thormód to him.

Then Skúf said: "You act most shortsightedly, farmer Thorkel, if you want to slay Thormód, your own guest and the skald of King Ólaf. You will pay dearly for the man if the king hears that you had him killed, and especially so since he was sent to you that you should protect and support him. This shows what so often is the case, that rage can blind a man. Now we shall offer you compensation in Thormód's behalf for this slaying and the loss you have incurred by it."

Thorkel was calmed down by these words of Skúf. Many men had a share in arranging a settlement between them. So it came about that Skúf undertook to assure Thorkel the right to make his own award in compensation for the slaying of Lodin. Thereupon Thormód went to Stockness as the guest of Skúf and Biarni.

XXIII · THORMÓD AVENGES THORGEIR ON THORGRÍM. HE SLAYS THORGRÍM'S SONS. GRÍMA CONCEALS THORMÓD FROM THORDÍS

EGIL was the name of one of Skúf's servants. He was a big and strong fellow, ugly, unhandy, and stupid. He was known as Fool-Egil. Thormód was gloomy for a long time, and Biarni and Skúf asked him whether they could do anything to help him overcome his depression.

Thormód answered: "I wish you would procure me a man to attend me and follow me wherever I want to go."

They said that he should have his way and asked him to choose among their servants whomever he would.

Thormód said: "Then I choose Fool-Egil, because he is big and strong and not too smart for doing whatever I bid him."

They told him he could have Egil, but wondered why he had chosen him.

Biarni fashioned a battle-axe for Thormód according to his directions. It was hammered of one piece from head to edge, without a weal, and was as sharp as a knife.[1]

The summer after these events took place, people went to the Assembly at Gardar in the Einars Firth. The people from the Eiriks Firth had covered their booths,[2] and there was a rise in the ground between their booths and those of the people from the Einars Firth. When the men were almost finished with this task Thorgrím still had not arrived, but he was soon seen approaching in his magnificent ship. Its crew also was warlike and well-equipped. Thorgrím's manner was so overbearing that people hardly dared to talk to him. The Greenlanders were accustomed to have their fishing gear with them on their boats at all times.

Now when Thorgrím's ship made land people went to the beach to admire the brave show and the equipment of the crew. Thormód stood there too. He picked up a seal-harpoon someone had hurled from the ship, and was examining it, but one of Thorgrím's followers grabbed it from him and said: "Unhand the harpoon, man! Because it won't be of any use to you even though you keep it, for I am thinking you don't know how to handle a harpoon."

Thormód answered: "I am not so sure you know better than I."

"There is little doubt about that," answered the other man. Then Thormód spoke this verse:

> 20. Than I better, boasts the
> Balder-of-shields,[3] could he
> handle the seal-harpoon—
> hard he runs o'er rock-shelves :[4]
> well I wot whom first the
> winsomest of princes[5]—
> gold he gave a-plenty—
> gathered in his shield-wall.

Then he went up to Thorgrím's booth which was being set up with great splendor and fine furnishings.

It so happened one day at the Assembly when the weather was fine that all the men had left the booth belonging to Skúf and Biarni. Only Thormód remained behind and slept. He had covered himself with his fur cloak which was of two colors, white on the inside and black on the outside. After sleeping a while he awoke and noticed that everybody was gone. He wondered about that because the booth had been full when he fell asleep.

At that moment Egil came rushing into the booth and said: "You are missing some great entertainment."

Thormód asked: "Where do you come from, and what kind of entertainment is there?"

Egil answered: "I was at the booth of Thorgrím Einarsson, and almost all people of the Assembly are there right now."

Thormód said: "And what is the entertainment there?"

Egil said: "Thorgrím is telling a story." Thormód said: "About whom is the story he is telling?"

Egil said: "I don't know exactly about whom the story is, but he tells it well and entertainingly. He is sitting on a chair by his booth, and the people are sitting around him and listening to him."

Thormód said: "You surely can mention someone figuring in the story, especially since you think it is so good!"

Egil said: "Someone called Thorgeir occurred in it, a big fighter; and I seem to remember that Thorgrím had something to do in it and was foremost in the fray, as one might expect. I wish you would go there and listen to his story."[6]

"I think I shall," Thormód said. He rose up and put on his cloak, turning the black side out. He pulled down the hood and took his axe in hand. Then both went to Thorgrím's booth. They placed themselves by the wall of the booth and tried to listen, but they could not understand very well what was said.

The weather had been fine until then, with bright sunshine; but when Thormód arrived at the booth the sky began to cloud up. Thormód kept looking up into the sky and then at the ground before him.

Egil said: "What are you doing that for?"

Thormód answered: "Because the sky looks as though there might be a big crash coming, and the ground looks that way too."

Egil said: "Just why should there be such a big crash?"

Thormód answered: "Such a big crash always heralds great events. Now if it so happens that you hear a big crash, then take care of yourself the best you can and run back to our booth as fast as your legs will carry you, and take shelter there."

While they were still talking there came a heavy shower with strong gusts of wind. Everybody took to his heels, each to his own booth, because no one had expected rain. A number of men went into Thorgrím's booth, and there was much crowding about the door. Thorgrím remained sitting on his chair, waiting till the throng about the door had cleared a little.

Thormód said to Egil: "Wait here! But I shall go to the front of the booth and see what might happen. And if you hear a big crash, then run back to our booth the fastest you can."

So Thormód went to the front of the booth where Thorgrím sat.

Thormód said: "What was the story you were telling?"

Thorgrím answered: "That is not told so easily in a few words; it deals with such great events. For that matter, what is your name?"

Thormód said: "I am called Ótrygg."[7]

"And whose son are you?" asked Thorgrím.

"I am the son of Tortrygg."

Then Thorgrím started to get up from his chair, but Thormód dealt him a blow on his head and cleft it down to the shoulders. Then he hid the axe under his cloak and laid Thorgrím's head on his lap and cried out: "This way, men, someone has slain Thorgrím."

Then many crowded around and saw what deed had been committed. They asked if he knew who had killed Thorgrím.

Thormód answered: "I saw him a moment ago, but I ran

quickly to support Thorgrím when he was cut down, and did not see where the fellow ran who killed him. Some of you come and support Thorgrím while others hunt for the man who has done this."

Then they supported Thorgrím, but Thormód walked off and along the shore. And behind a headland he turned his cloak inside out so the white showed.

When Egil had heard the crash of the blow which Thormód dealt Thorgrím he ran back to his booth. The followers of Skúf spied him running and guessed it was he who had slain Thorgrím. Egil was frightened to death when he saw men pursuing him with weapons in their hands. And when they captured him he trembled like a leaf. But as soon as they saw it was Egil they felt sure that he was not the man to have slain Thorgrím. And then his fear left him as the heat leaves iron.[8]

The people searched all the booths for the slayer but did not find him. Then they followed the shoreline to where the headland jutted into the sea, and there they met a man in a white fur cloak. They asked him who he was, and he said his name was Vígfús.[9] They asked him where he was going.

He answered: "I am looking for the man who slew Thorgrím."

They and Thormód were going opposite ways and mighty fast, so there was soon a distance between them. Now Skúf and Biarni missed Thormód, and they thought it not so unlikely that he had slain Thorgrím, because when in Norway Skúf had overheard the king's remarks about avenging the death of Thorgeir Hávarsson. When most of the commotion had died down they secretly procured a boat and put some provisions in it. They rowed around the headland as they had heard it said that a man in a white fur cloak had been seen there who called himself Vígfús. And when they rounded the headland they caught sight of Thormód. They rowed ashore and called out to him to get into the boat. He did so, and they asked him if he had slain Thorgrím. He said that he had. They asked him how great the wound might be which he had dealt him. Then Thormód spoke this verse:

21. Thorgrím, fated to fall, was
    felled by one left-handed:
    gone to pot[10] were the poet's
    pride—often that happens—
    if my axe too feebly
    the urger-of-the-sword-storm's[11]
    swarthy pate had smitten:
    sudden death I dealt him!

"Very possibly," said Thormód, "the blow was not a hard
one, because it was dealt by a left-handed man. But I did not
strike a second time because I thought the first one sufficient."

Then Skúf said: "You were lucky they did not recognize
you when you had Thorgrím's head on your lap, and also
when they met you up on the headland."

Then Thormód spoke this verse:

22. Strange is't that the storm-of-
    steel's-impellers[11] knew me
    not, well-known though was my
    voice and blackish hair-bush:
    saved was I since, than the
    serpents-hoard's-dispenser's,[12]
    a longer life was given[13] to
    lean-mouthed-axe's-wielder.

[14]"I am easy to recognize," he said, "with my black, curly
hair, and stammering as I do; but I was not fated to die that
time, and it may be that I escaped for some purpose and that
some kinsmen of Thorgrím's will bite the dust before I do."

Biarni said: "It would be well now to let matters stand as
they are, for you have done your share about avenging Thorgeir."

Then Thormód spoke this verse:

24. Vie with many—vengeance
    vowed I and did sate the
    ravening wolves—I would not,
    warrior! to avenge him:

my axe—their share let others
also do now—brought I—
I have done my duty—
down on Thorgrím's helm-block.[15]

"It would seem to me," said Biarni, "that you need do no
more about avenging Thorgeir, because you have done a
great deed, foreigner as you are here, single-handed to have
laid low the greatest chieftain but one in all Greenland; nor is
it so sure that you can escape, because Thorgrím has many
energetic kinsmen surviving him who are great fighters."

Thereupon they took Thormód to the Eiriks Firth and
conducted him to a cave which is now called Thormód's
Cave. This cave is in the sea-cliff on the opposite side of the
firth from Stockness. There are steep rocks both above and
below the cave, and it is difficult to reach it either way. Skúf
and Biarni said to Thormód: "Stay in this cave now. We
shall come to see you as soon as the Assembly is over." Then
they returned to the Assembly.

Thormód was missed at the Assembly, and people began
to suspect that it was he who had slain Thorgrím. Bodvar and
Falgeir brought suit against him and he was made an outlaw
because of the slaying. Skúf and Biarni went to see Thormód
to bring him food and other things he needed and told him
about his being made an outlaw. They urged him to remain
there, because he would be safe nowhere once his hiding place
became known. They said they would come now and again to
visit him.

There was a large grass plot in front of the cave mouth,
and it was just possible for an agile person to leap down upon
it from above. Thormód became bored with staying in the
cave, for there was little to entertain him there; and one fine
day he left the cave and climbed the cliff, taking his axe with
him. And when he had come a short way from the cave he
met a man. He was large and uncouth looking, ugly and un-
prepossessing in appearance. About him he had a cloak which
was sewed together of many tatters, as crinkly as a sheep's
stomach, with a hood on it of the same kind, lousy all over.
Thormód asked him who he was.

He answered: "My name is Oddi."

Thormód said: "What is your business?"

He answered: "I am a serf and am called Louse Oddi. I don't care to work, but I'm no liar, nor a fool, either, and good people always treat me well. And what is your name?"

Thormód answered: "I am called Torrád."[16]

Oddi asked: "And what kind of person are you, Torrád?"

He answered: "I am a merchant. How about trading with me, Oddi?"

He replied: "I have nothing to trade. What would you trade with me?"

"I want to have the cloak you are wearing."

Oddi said: "You don't need to make fun of me."

Thormód said: "I don't mean to make fun of you. Let me give you my cloak, and you let me have yours and deliver my message to Stockness and get there by evening. Tell Skúf and Biarni that you met a man today who called himself Torrád and that he exchanged clothes with you. There is no other message. You may keep my cloak if you deliver this message."

Oddi answered: "It isn't an easy matter to get across the firth, because one needs a boat for that. Still, I may manage to do so and get to Stockness this evening."

Then they exchanged cloaks, Oddi put on the black one, and Torrád, the ragged one.

Then Thormód went to the Einars Firth and encountered the shepherd of Thordís on Longness. He asked him whether the sons of Thordís were at home.

The shepherd answered: "Bodvar is not at home, but his brothers were here last night; but now they are out rowing to catch fish."

Thormód said: "Very likely."

The shepherd thought he was talking to Louse Oddi. Then they parted, and Thormód went to the boathouse of Thordís and stayed there.

As evening came on Thormód could see the brothers rowing landward. Thorkel rowed forward in the prow, Thórd amidships, and Falgeir, low in the stern. When the boat

touched shore Thorkel stood up in the stem, intending to
jump out and make the boat fast. Then Thormód came out of
the boathouse, and the brothers thought it was Louse Oddi
they saw. Then Thormód suddenly made for Thorkel, and
with both hands dealt him a blow on the head, splitting his
skull. He died then and there.

Then Thormód fled and threw off his cloak. Thórd and
Falgeir ran after him. Thormód put on great speed, running
toward the sea-cliff above the cave, and there he leaped from
above down on the grass strip in front of the cave entrance.
And no sooner did he land on it but Thórd leaped after him;
but when he landed on the grass his knees buckled under him
so he lurched forward. Right then Thormód struck him between the shoulders so that his axe was buried to the shaft.
But before he could pull the axe out of the wound Falgeir
leaped from above and immediately delivered a blow at Thormód. It landed between his shoulders and made a big wound.
Then Thormód gripped Falgeir about his middle, because
now he was weaponless. But now he found that he lacked
strength to use against Falgeir and was in a dangerous situation, being both wounded and without arms. Then he bethought himself of King Ólaf, hoping that the king's good
fortune would aid him,[17] when suddenly the axe fell out of
Falgeir's hand and into the sea below. Then Thormód felt the
situation to be not so hopeless as before since both now were
without arms.

And then both fell off the cliff into the sea. There, they
tried their powers in swimming, ducking one another. Thormód felt his strength failing on account of his wound and the
loss of blood. But because Thormód was not fated to die it so
happened that Falgeir's belt burst, and Thormód pulled his
trousers down about his feet. That made swimming difficult
for Falgeir. He went down time and again and swallowed
much sea water. Finally only his buttocks and shoulders
showed above water, and when he died his face came up.
Mouth and eyes were open, and his face looked as if he were
grinning about something. The end was that Falgeir was
drowned.

Thormód was almost exhausted by then. He swam to a skerry[18] and crawled up on the shingle and lay there, expecting to die, because he had a great wound and was tired to death and it was far to land.

Now we must tell about Louse Oddi. As had been agreed between him and Thormód, he came to Skúf and Biarni and told them that he had met a man on his way that day who called himself Torrád and who had exchanged his cloak with him, that he should go to Stockness and tell Skúf and Biarni that he had met him and about their shifting clothes. They recognized Thormód's cloak and gathered that the reason Thormód had sent Louse Oddi to them was that he had some daring deed in mind.

That night they took a boat secretly and rowed across the firth. And when they drew near to the cave they saw something move on a skerry and wondered whether it was a seal or what else it could be. So they rowed toward the skerry and went up on it and saw a man lying there and recognized Thormód. They asked him what had happened, and he told them about the events of that night.

Skúf said: "Truly, it was not for nothing that you got away from the Assembly at Gardar, since in one night you have been the death of three fighters, all men of high degree."

Thormód said: "One thing only was in my mind before you came here—that I was going to die on this skerry. But now it seems not unlikely to me that I may recover; and then it may be indeed that I have not escaped for nothing."

They asked him about his struggle with Falgeir. Then Thormód spoke this verse:

> 25. Trod I water still, when
> strangely gaped the booby's
> ars-cleft o'er the surface—
> honorless then died he:
> hateful haggard eyes the
> half-wit set on me, and
> grinning, ghastly leered the
> Gaut-of-battle[19] toward me.

Skúf and Biarni carried Thormód to the boat on a sheet, because he could not walk. Then they got his clothing and provisions out of the cave, for they knew he could stay there no longer, and rowed into the Eiriks Firth with him.

There, at the very end of the firth, right under the glacier, lived a man called Gamli. He had little property and lived apart from people. He was a great hunter. His wife was called Gríma, a proud-minded woman, skilled in many things, a good healer, and somewhat versed in witchcraft. No one else lived there. They rarely saw other people, and few came to see them. Skúf and Biarni rowed their boat ashore a little distance from their house. Skúf went up to it while Biarni took care of Thormód. They welcomed Skúf and offered him entertainment.

He said: "We have a wounded man with us, and I would that you cured him."

Gríma said: "Who is the man?"

Skúf answered: "Thormód, a skald and follower of King Ólaf, and he is badly wounded."

"Who gave him the wound?" she asked.

Then Skúf told her what had happened.

"These are events of much consequence," she said, "and he has gotten himself into great difficulties. It seems a great risk to take in a man who has been outlawed by the kin of Thorgrím, and all the more so after he has done such deeds while an outlaw."

Skúf said: "I shall pay for any harm done to you on his account, in case any charge is made against you in this business; and I shall make up for any outlay you incur for him."

And their talk ended by Gríma agreeing to take Thormód in. He was brought up to the house, and Gríma cleansed and bandaged his wounds, and he soon felt somewhat better. Skúf and Biarni thereupon rowed back to Stockness.

The news of these events seemed shocking to everybody. The entire truth about them was not learned immediately, for many thought at first that Thormód was drowned at the same spot where Falgeir's body was found. Thormód's wounds did not heal quickly, and he did not recover from it for fully a year. And when a year had passed after these events he was able to walk between the kitchen and the living room, and yet his wound had not healed altogether.

It happened one night the following spring that Thordís on Longness was restless in her sleep, and some said they ought to wake her.

But her son Bodvar said: "Let my mother have her dream out. For it may be that something is revealed to her which she would like to know."

So they did not wake her. And when she did awake she breathed heavily.

Then her son Bodvar said: "You carried on in your sleep, mother. Was anything revealed to you?"

Thordís answered: "Far did I ride my magic staff this night; and I have got to know things that I did not know before."[20]

Bodvar said: "What things?"

Thordís answered: "Thormód who killed my sons and your brothers is alive, and he is staying with Gamli and Gríma, at the head of the Eiriks Firth. Now I am going to find them and catch Thormód and repay him with a vile death for the great harm he has done us. We will go to Brattahlíd and ask Thorkel to go with us, for he will resent it if any wrong is done to Gamli and Gríma, since he has always held his hand over them."

Bodvar declared he was ready to go whenever she wanted. They got up at night and launched a large boat they owned and went aboard it, fifteen altogether, and rowed into the Eiriks Firth. It was the time of the year when the nights were light enough for traveling.

Now at the same time that Thordís and her company had started on their journey, Gríma—so we are told—carried on in her sleep. Thormód was for waking her, but Gamli answered: "Gríma would not like to be waked, because in her sleep she often gets to know things which she considers of importance to her."

They said no more. Gríma awoke soon afterwards.

Then Gamli said: "You were restless in your sleep, Gríma. Was anything revealed to you?"

Gríma answered: "This was the thing made known to me: Thordís from Longness has started out with fifteen of her men and means to come here; because through her witchcraft she has found out that Thormód is here with us, and she intends to kill him. Now I want you, Gamli, to stay home today and not go hunting, because there aren't too many here with the two of you, and fifteen men coming to ransack the house; especially since Thormód is not strong enough to fight. And yet I don't have the heart to send you two up into the mountains. Rather, I want you to stay at home."

Now Thordís journeyed on in the night till she came to Brattahlíd. Thorkel received them in friendly fashion and asked them to stay.

Thordís said: "My errand here is that I am going to look up Gamli and Gríma, who belong to your district, because I have learned that Thormód is there, the man whom we have outlawed and who, many think, was drowned. Now it is my wish that you go with us and see to it that we get our rights with Gamli and Gríma. You will know exactly what our quarrel is when you hear what is said."

Thorkel answered: "It seems unlikely to me that Gríma is giving shelter to the man you have outlawed. Still I shall go with you if you so wish."

Thereupon Thordís and her company ate their morning meal there. Meanwhile Thorkel gathered his men, for he did not care to be at the mercy of Thordís and Bodvar, in case of a clash with them. When the men had eaten their fill Thorkel went aboard his boat with twenty men, and both companies departed without further argument.

Gamli's wife Gríma had a large chair, and on the posts of it there was carved a large-size image of Thór. That morning Gríma said: "Now I shall tell you what is to be done today. I shall set my chair in the middle of the living room, and I shall want you, Thormód, to sit in it when the men approach. And I don't want you to get up out of it while Thordís is here. Even if you see some strange things happen and if your life

is threatened, don't get up out of it. Because if you are fated
to die it will not help to crouch in a corner. Gamli is to hang
the kettle over the fire and boil seal meat in it, and you are to
throw trash on the fire so as to make a great smoke in the
house. I myself shall sit in the doorway and spin my yarn and
talk with those who come."

Everything was done as she ordered. And when the boats
of Thorkel and Thordís were seen to approach Thormód sat
down in the chair. Gamli had hung the kettle over the fire and
put trash on it so as to fill the house with smoke, and with it
came a great darkness so that one could not see anything.[21]
Gríma sat on the threshold and span and murmured words
the others could not understand.

Meanwhile the boats made land and the men went up to
the homestead, and Thorkel with them. Gríma welcomed him
and asked him to stay.

Thorkel said: "Thordís from Longness has come here
with us, and she maintains that Thormód, whom she has outlawed, is staying here with you. We want you to hand him
out to us if you know where he is; because it is beyond your
power to hold an outlaw against Thordís and her son Bodvar."

Gríma answered: "It seems strange to me that Thordís
thinks that I could hold an outlaw against people so powerful
as those on Longness, considering that I have no one else in
the house but my husband."

"It certainly is strange," said Thorkel, "yet we mean to
search your premises."

Gríma said: "You would be welcome to search my place,
even if you did not have such a crowd of people with you. I
am always pleased to see you in my house, but I would not
like to have those people from the Einars Firth proceed with
violence and do damage about my property."

Thorkel said: "Thordís and I, we two alone, will search
the premises."

And so they did. They entered and searched, nor did it
take them long, for the property was quite small. They
opened the door into the living room and found it full of

smoke, and they saw nothing out of the ordinary. The whole place was rank with smoke, so they stayed there a rather shorter time than they would have done if the air had been pure. So they came out and searched all the premises outside.

Then Thordís said: "There was so much smoke that I could not make out clearly what all was in the living room. Let us get up on the roof and take off the louvers so the smoke can pass out, and then see what is in the living room."

So Bodvar and Thordís climbed on the roof and took off the louvers. The smoke passed out and they could see everything there was in the living room. They could see Gríma's chair standing in the middle of the room and Thór with his hammer carved on the posts of the chair, but they could not see Thormód. They came down from the roof again and went to the door.

Then Thordís said: "There still is some heathendom about Gríma since the image of Thór is carved on the posts of her chair."

Gríma replied: "I seldom get to go to church to hear the teaching of priests, for it is a long way and I have no one else in the house; but it often occurs to me when I see this image of Thór made of wood, that I could break it to pieces and burn it whenever I wanted to, and how much more powerful is he who made heaven and earth and all things visible and invisible and gave life to all and that no one can overcome him."

Thordís answered: "It may be that these are your thoughts; but I rather think we might force you to say more if Thorkel were not here with so great a number of men. Because something tells me that you know pretty well where Thormód is."

Gríma answered: "Now is borne out the proverb which says 'there's many a miss for people who guess,' and also this one: 'he who is not fated to die will escape somehow.' But what you require is heavenly keeping lest the devil entice you to do the wicked things you had meant to do. Because it is excusable that one sometimes fails to see things as they are,

but it is inexcusable for anyone not to believe the truth once
he has found it to be the truth."

After these words they parted. Thorkel returned to Brattahlíd and Thordís, to her home. Skúf and Biarni secretly
came to see Gamli and Gríma. They brought such goods as
they needed and amply repaid them for the expenses they had
with Thormód.

XXIV · THORMÓD AND SIGURD ATTACK LIÓT. THORMÓD ESCAPES THORDÍS' PURSUIT AND SLAYS LIÓT. THORMÓD REJOINS KING ÓLAF. THORMÓD'S DEATH AT STIKLASTAD

WHEN Thormód had recovered from the wound which
Falgeir had given him, Skúf and Biarni brought him to
Stockness and kept him in hiding in a storehouse, and there
Thormód remained during the third winter. That same winter Skúf and Biarni sold their farm on Stockness as well as
other landed property, together with their livestock, because
they intended to leave Greenland. Early in spring they got
their ship ready and launched it. Then Thormód was eager to
leave the storehouse. He said he had some errand on the
north side of the firth. He got himself a boat, and Fool-Egil
was to go with him. He plied the oars while Thormód steered.
Egil was a good oarsman and an excellent swimmer. The
weather was clear and beautiful, with sunshine and a gentle
breeze. They rowed into the Eiriks Firth. But when they had
rowed some way Thormód became very restless, moving
around and rocking the boat now this way, now that.

Egil said: "Why are you carrying on so foolishly like a
crazy person? Do you want to upset us?"

Thormód said: "I feel so uneasy."

Egil said: "I can't row if you carry on so, and you must not behave so crazily as to upset the boat."

But whatever Egil said, in the end Thormód did upset the boat. He dived and swam away from the boat and kept that up till he reached land. He had his axe with him. Egil managed to climb up on the keel. There he rested and looked about him if he could see Thormód, but he was nowhere to be seen. Then Egil got the boat righted again and took to the oars and rowed back out of the firth till he came back to Stockness. There he told Skúf and Biarni what had happened and ended his story by saying he believed Thormód was dead. They thought this a strange occurrence and wondered whether things really had happened that way. They had their doubts whether Thormód really was drowned.

Now to tell about Thormód, what he did when he reached land. First, he wrung out his clothes. Then he started walking, and late in the afternoon arrived at Sigríd's farm at Hamar. There he knocked at the door. A woman came out and greeted him, then turned to go back into the living room. Thormód followed her and seated himself near the door on the lower bench.[1]

Sigríd addressed him and said: "Who is it that came there?"

He answered: "My name is Ósvíf."[2]

Sigríd said: "As name, so fame.[3] Does Ósvíf wish to stay here overnight?"

He said he would like to.

Next morning Sigríd went to speak with him and asked him what his business might be.

Thormód answered: "I spoke truly yesterday when I named myself Ósvíf."

She answered: "I thought I knew you though I have not seen you before. You are Thormód the skald of Coal-Brow."

He answered: "It will not do to deny it since you have recognized me. My business is to go to Thórunn, the daughter of Einar, on Longness and there find her son Liót. Both have said much ill of me."[4]

Sigríd said: "Then my son Sigurd shall go with you, because both Liót and Thórunn have often dealt harshly with me too."

Thormód said: "I hardly think it advisable for Sigurd to go with me, because the two of you would not be able to maintain yourselves on your farm here if anything should happen to him in the fight with Liót."

"Gladly would I leave the farm," said Sigríd, "if only Liót is humbled."

So Sigurd went along with Thormód to Thórunn on Longness. They knocked at the door, and a woman came out and greeted them. Sigurd asked her if Liót was at home.

She answered: "He is in the living room."

Sigurd said: "Ask him to come out."

The servant woman went back in and asked Liót to go to the door. He said: "Who told you?"

"Sigurd from Hamar," she said, "and another man I didn't know."

"How did the man look whom you did not know?"

She answered: "He had curly black hair."

Liót said: "Then he resembles our enemy, Thormód."

He went to the door, and the women who were there went with him. He had a spear in his hand as he approached the door. He recognized Thormód and thrust at him immediately, aiming at his breast. Thormód parried the thrust with his axe, deflecting it so that it struck below the knee, where it made a big wound. Liót lurched forward as he thrust at Thormód, and Sigurd dealt him a blow between the shoulders, inflicting a large wound. He ran back into the house, and the women in front of him. Thormód and Sigurd then retired.

Thormód told Sigurd to return to Hamar, "and tell your mother what has happened; but I shall take care of myself." So they parted, and Sigurd went home to Hamar and told his mother how things had gone.

Sigríd said: "My advice is that you go to Skúf and call upon him to look out for you. Tell him that I want to sell my land and leave Greenland with him."

So Sigurd went to Skúf and brought up his request. Skúf

took him in. He sold Sigríd's land and moved her property to his ship.

Thormód bandaged his wound and went to the boathouse Thórunn had. He saw that a boat had been moved out of it and concluded that Thórunn's men-servants were out rowing. Thormód went down to the shore and made himself a bed in a heap of seaweed and lay there during the day. When evening came he could hear the noise of oars and saw that Thórunn's men had come to land. He overheard them say: "The weather will be good tomorrow for us to row out, so let us not beach our boat but let it float in the harbor overnight."

They did so. By that time it had grown quite dark. As soon as the men had gone up to the farm Thormód arose and undid the ropes. Then he applied himself to the oars and rowed out in the direction of the farm at Vík.[5]

That same evening Thordís in Longness lay down to sleep and slept very restlessly. When she awoke she called out:

"Where is my son Bodvar?"

He answered: "Here I am, mother; what do you want of me?"

She answered: "I want you to go with me in the boat, for there is the chance of a good catch."

"What kind of catch?" said Bodvar.

Thordís said: "Thormód, whom we have outlawed, is out on the firth rowing by himself, and we must go to find him."

Five men-servants went with Thordís as they rowed out on the firth in the night. Thormód heard the beat of oars and suspected that Thordís had set out with her men. He knew that his case was desperate if they found him. There was an islet not far distant. It was low and was covered with water at high tide but not between tides. The idea occurred to him to capsize the boat and swim to the island. There was much seaweed all around it. He dug himself in between two rocks and heaped seaweed upon himself. As Thordís and her company were rowing in the darkness they saw some black object on the water. They rowed that way to see what it was and found that it was an overturned boat. The oars were still in the rowlocks.

Then the men with Thordís said: "Here is where Thormód must have hit a rock and very likely was drowned."

Thordís said: "I don't believe he was drowned. Rather, I think he heard us coming and himself overturned the boat, and did that to make us believe that he was dead. Very likely he swam to the island and hid there. So let us row there and search it. Now I want you to poke into all places all over the island, and more than once."

They did what she told them to, but he was not to be found. Then it seemed unlikely to them that he was there.

But Thordís said: "I feel sure that he is on this island even though you don't find him. Now if Thormód can hear me, then let him answer me if he has a man's heart rather than a mare's."[6]

Thormód heard what she said and wanted to answer her but could not, because it was as if someone stopped his mouth. As soon as they were gone he rose up out of the seaweed and swam in the direction where it seemed shortest to the mainland. He stopped at the skerries on the way to rest; and when he still had but a short way to go he reached a skerry but was so exhausted that he could not go on.

That same night farmer Grím[7] in Vík dreamed that a man appeared to him. He was handsome and distinguished-looking, of middle height, thick-set and broad-shouldered. He asked Grím whether he was awake or slept.

He answered: "I am awake; but who are you?"

The man said: "I am King Ólaf Haraldsson;[8] and my business is to tell you that you must go and look for Thormód, my follower and skald, and give him help so that he may get away from the place where he is lying on a skerry not far from land. And as a proof that this is true I will tell you that the foreigner who has been staying with you this winter[9] and calls himself Gest, really is called Steinar, or Helgu-Steinar,[10] and is an Icelander who came to Greenland because he wanted to avenge Thorgeir Hávarsson. But though Steinar is a brave and dauntless man yet he is not destined to have much success in the business of avenging Thorgeir; but his bravery will stand him in good stead on other occasions."[11]

After King Ólaf had spoken thus Grím awoke. He awakened Gest and bade him get up. He did so and took his weapons in hand and went out with Grím. They sat down, and Grím said: "What did you say your name was?"

Gest said: "You will remember, Grím, that I told you."

Grím replied: "To be sure I remember what you called yourself; but I am asking you whether your name is really what you said it was."

Gest answered: "Why not?"

Grím said: "Because your name is Steinar, and you are called Helgu-Steinar in your own country."

Gest said: "Who told you this?"

Grím replied: "King Ólaf."

Gest said: "When did you meet King Ólaf?"

Then Grím told him his dream.

Steinar said: "Your dream is true so far as I am concerned."

Then both went to look for Thormód, and they found him on the spot which Ólaf had indicated to Grím and brought him home to Vík and there secretly took care of him and healed his wounds.

As soon as Thormód had fully recovered from the wounds Liót had given him, Steinar brought him to the ship owned by Skúf and Biarni. Skúf himself was not on board at the time. Steinar was all ready to leave Vík, but remained on the ship with Thormód. Skúf tarried a long time, waiting for the Assembly to end. There, Bodvar, the son of Thordís, caused Sigurd, the son of Sigríd, to be made an outlaw because he had wounded Liót.

After the Assembly had come to an end Skúf was ready to depart. But on the very morning he intended to sail, Thormód and Gest, without Skúf's permission, took a boat and rowed into the Einars Firth till they came close to Thórunn's farm. There they saw four men sitting in a boat fishing, Liót among them, the son of Thórunn. They attacked them at once; and the outcome of the fight was that Liót was killed as well as all the men in his boat. Then Thormód and Gest rowed back to the ship, where Skúf was all ready to hoist sail. Thormód and Skúf went aboard their ship, but Steinar remained behind. He went to stay with Thorkel at Brattahlíd. Skúf and Biarni put out to sea. They had favorable breezes and a good journey to Norway. As soon as they had moored their ship, they divided their possessions. And out of their common property, Biarni had the ship and Skúf the movable possessions. Biarni sailed south to Denmark and from there went to Rome on a pilgrimage to the tombs of Saint Peter and Paul; and on that journey he died. Sigríd and her son Sigurd bought lands in Norway and lived there till their dying days. Skúf and Thormód went to join the king and remained with him until the end of their days.

At first the king was not well disposed toward Thormód. A man had come to the king's court by the name of Grím. He was an Icelander and claimed to have avenged Thorgeir Hávarsson before Thormód did. The king showed him great favor and gave him presents. But Thormód found out about him that he was a scoundrel and had murdered a man in Iceland. Then Thormód went before the king and spoke a verse:

> 26. Goods you gave far more to
> Grím—squibs oft are made—but
> fewer far to me, sire,
> fairly than was needful:
> dog's work he has done—a
> dastard who will do such—
> while deeds of derring-do I
> did for my and your fame.

The king said: "So you, Thormód, think you accomplished more in Greenland than Grím in Iceland?"

Thormód answered: "Assuredly."

King Ólaf said: "What deeds of mark did you perform in Greenland?"

Thormód answered:

> 27. Thorgrím overthrew I:
> there fell a warrior!
> Ere that, arrow-combat's-
> urger,[12] I slew Lodin.

> Then I Thorkel slaughtered;
> Thórd died as the fourth one:
> foremost of them, Falgeir
> felled I to the ground then.

King Ólaf said: "You have done more in the way of man-slaughter than the fisherman who considers that he has done his share when he catches a fish for himself, another for his boat, a third for his fish-hook, and a fourth for his line. You did better than that. But why did you make away with so many men?"

Thormód answered: "I resented their comparisons: they likened me to a mare and said that I was among men as a mare among stallions."

The king said: "No wonder you resented their malicious speech; and you did settle accounts with them."

Then Thormód spoke a verse:

> 28. Burnt I have a blaze most
> baleful on Greenlanders—
> heavy harm I did them—
> who had made me outlaw:
> long will remain that mark on
> mighty sword-fight-workers'
> hulks, nor easy healed the
> harm—unless they slay me.

"Very true," said the king; "it will be a long time before they will forget the lesson you taught them."

Now Thormód stood in high favor with the king and proved himself most valiant in all trying circumstances. He accompanied King Ólaf on his journeys abroad and was with him the entire time he was exiled from his country.[13] And he returned with him to Norway, for he considered it better to die with him than to live after him. Now when the king arrived in the Drontheim district and came into the valley which is called Vera Dale, and when he became aware that the inhabitants of that valley were lying in wait for him, he asked Thormód jokingly: "What would your counsel be if you were heading the force which we have here?"

Then Thormód spoke this verse:

29. Burn all buildings with the
birches'-sorrow,[14] and people,
since with sword the yeomen
seem to guard their homesteads;
fire should fall in brambles,
flames consume the homes—if
I had aught to say—of
all rebellious Thronders.

King Ólaf said: "Very possibly it might be feasible to do as you say;[15] still, we shall follow other counsel than to burn our own land ourselves. But I have no doubt that you would do as you say."

On the day of the Battle of Stiklastad[16] the king asked Thormód to recite some poem to entertain the troops. And he recited the *Old Lay of Biarki*.[17]

The king said: "Well chosen is the poem you have recited because of the events which will take place here today. I shall give it the title of *Exhortation of the Housecarls*."

We are told that Thormód was rather depressed on the day before the battle. The king observed it and said: "Why are you so silent, Thormód?"

He answered: "For the reason, sire, that I am not sure that we two shall occupy the same lodgings for the night. But if you promise me that we shall find our rest in the same place,[18] then I shall be cheerful."

King Ólaf said: "I do not know whether I shall be able to bring that about; but if I do, then you shall be with me to-night."

Then Thormód became cheerful and spoke a verse:

30. Draweth nigh the dreaded
dart-storm,[19] arrow-sender!
Quake nor cringe, ye dauntless
king's-men—waxeth sword-din:[19]
whether now, king, we hence do
hie us, giving ravens—
foreordained our fate is—
food, or lie on battle-field.

The king answered: "It may well turn out, skald, as you say, that the men who are here now may either escape alive or else remain on the battlefield."

Then Thormód spoke a verse:

31. Stay would I still with thee,
     steerer-of-ships, till other
     skalds thou hast—but when dost
     hope they come?—and fend thee:
     gladly would I, gallant—
     gory shields we carry—
     wielder-of-the-wound-snake,[20]
     with thee live and die eke!

King Ólaf said: "You seem to be making insinuations about our skald Sigvat; but that is uncalled for, because he would have wished to be here if he could have known what is about to happen in this place.[21] Who knows but that it is he who may be of greatest use to us?"[22]

Thormód answered: "That may well be; but I am thinking that few would be rallying about your banner today if many had gone his way."

Great praise has been bestowed on Thormód for his brave fight at Stiklastad, where King Ólaf fell; for he carried neither shield nor coat of mail but hewed away steadily, wielding the battle-axe with both his hands and cutting through the enemy's troops; and no one whom he met liked to find his night's rest under his axe. We are told that when the battle was over Thormód still was not wounded.

That distressed him greatly, and he said: "I fear now that I may not go to the same lodgings as the king this evening. But worse it seems to me now to live than to die."

And the very moment he said this an arrow came flying at him and pierced his breast, and he did not know whence it came. This wound gladdened him, for he felt sure it would be his death. He went to a barley barn where many king's men lay wounded. A woman was warming water to cleanse their wounds. Thormód went to a partition to lean against it.

The woman said to Thormód: "Are you a king's man, or do you belong to the franklins' party?"

Thormód spoke a verse:

> 32. Ólaf's man I am, and
> on me show I, white-clad
> woman, how with him fighting
> wounds I got, and truce none:
> shows my shield how in the
> shaft-storm[23] blasts assailed me:
> foemen's wands-of-wounds[24] had
> well-nigh killed the king's skald.

The woman said: "Why don't you have your wounds bandaged, if you are wounded?"

Thormód answered: "Such wounds have I only which require no bandaging."

The woman said: "What warriors fought best with the king today?"

Thormód spoke a verse:

> 33. Eager with open-handed
> Ólaf to fight was Harold;[25]
> by his side, the sword-play
> seeking, Dag and Ring[26] eke:
> stalwart beneath standards
> stood, with red war-shields—
> eagles drank there dead men's
> dark blood—twice twain sea-kings.

The woman asked Thormód still further: "How did the king bear himself in battle?"

Thormód spoke a verse:

> 34. Valiantly in van ad-
> vanced King Ólaf—bloody
> steels bit deep—at Stikla-
> stad; was battle welcome.
> Shields did shelter all from
> shower-of-arrows[27]—tried was
> many a man's stout heart in
> medley—but the leader.

Many men lay in the barn who had severe wounds, and there was a sound of much gurgling in them, as is the nature of wounds that pierce the body.[28] Now when Thormód had finished speaking these verses a man from the army of the franklins came into the barn. And when he heard the gurgling from the wounds he said: "It is not to be wondered at that the king did not do well in battle against the franklins, seeing he had such nerveless people as followers. Because I think it is safe to say that the men in here are hardly bearing their wounds without complaint."

Thormód said: "So you think the men who lie in here are nerveless?"

He answered: "It certainly does seem to me that many weak-kneed men have been gathered here."

Thormód said: "Very possibly there is someone in here in the barn who is not a hero. And perhaps you don't consider my wound to be serious?"

The franklin went up to Thormód in order to examine his wound. But Thormód swung his axe at him and gave him a great wound. He cried out and moaned aloud.

Then Thormód said: "I knew that someone in here was likely to be effeminate. It is ill befitting that you reproach others for their lack of courage and are nerveless yourself. Many men in here are badly wounded, yet no one moans. They can't help the gurgling in their wounds, but you cry and weep though you are only slightly hurt."

While he was saying this he leaned against a wall post in the barley barn. And when he had finished speaking the woman who was warming the water said to Thormód: "Why are you so pale, man, and ashen, like a ghost? Why don't you let me bandage your wounds?"

Thormód spoke a verse:

> 35. Red-cheeked nor ruddy is the
> reddener-of-swordblades;
> nor are, woman, the warrior's
> wounds tended by many.

> Sore do smart, thou giver-of-
> serpent's-gold, the wounds which
> Danish arms in Dag's Fray[29]
> dealt to the ring-breaker.

And when he had recited it he died standing up against the post and fell down dead. Harold Sigurdsson completed the stanza which Thormód recited, adding the last words. "For thus would he have meant to finish it."

Thus ended the life of Thormód, the skald of Coal-Brow, and thus ends the saga of Thormód the warrior of King Ólaf the Saint.

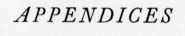

APPENDICES

APPENDICES.

APPENDIX 1 · THORGEIR'S ADVENTURE ON THE CLIFF

IT HAPPENED in the spring following that Thorgeir and Thormód journeyed northward along the Strands all the way to the Horn. And one day they went up the cliffs to look for Angelica;[1] and in a grassy spot, which since bears Thorgeir's name, they cut some big stalks of it. Thormód was to carry them up and Thorgeir was to remain below. Then the loose stones started sliding under Thorgeir's feet, and the only thing he could do was to grasp at an Angelica stalk and the grass around it and to hold on to the roots—else he would have plunged down. It was sixty ells down to the shingle on the beach. There was no possibility for him to climb up from that position, and so he hung there, yet would by no means call on Thormód to help him, even at the cost of falling; and that of course meant certain death.

Thormód waited on top of the cliff, thinking that Thorgeir would be coming up; but when it seemed to him that Thorgeir was taking so much longer time than could be expected he climbed down to the ledge where the slide had occurred and called and asked whether he was ever coming—whether he hadn't collected enough Angelica yet.

Thorgeir answered him then without a tremor in his voice and with a stout heart, "I think I shall have enough when the one is gone which I am holding on to."

Then Thormód suspected that Thorgeir might be in a helpless position. So he climbed down to the grass plot and became aware that Thorgeir was about to fall. He grabbed hold of him and hoisted him up—and by that time the Angelica stalk was nearly all pulled out. Then they went back to their fishing.

From this one can gather that Thorgeir was absolutely fearless and not afraid for his life; and on every occasion he acted bravely because of his strength, his valor, and other manly accomplishments. It is told that once upon a time all three, Thorgeir, Thormód, and Grettir the Strong, the son of Ásmund, were staying together at Reykiahólar, and that the

strength of the two and that of Grettir were about matched.[2]
It is also told that Thorgils said on the Mount of Laws at the
Althing, when asked about his guests that winter, whether
they were not the hardiest men in all Iceland and the most
fearless—that he said that this was not so, "because Grettir
is afraid of the dark, and Thormód fears God; but Thorgeir," he said, "was not afraid of anything whatsoever nor
of taking the most deadly risks."

Then they left the Strands with the catch they had made.
Thorgeir went home to Reykiahólar and Thormód to Laugaból.

APPENDIX 2 · THORMÓD AT THE COURT OF KING CANUTE. THORMÓD IS PARDONED BY KING ÓLAF AND BECOMES HIS MAN

THORMÓD, the skald of Coal-Brow, was a great gallant, a
man accomplished in many ways, a good skald, of medium
height, and exceedingly agile. He was greatly depressed after
the death of Thorgeir, his foster-brother. The same summer
that he was slain Thormód sailed from Vadil, and nothing is
told of the journey before the ship landed in Denmark.
Canute the Powerful[3] was king there at that time, and he was
told about Thormód, and how he surpassed all men in valor
and mettle as well as in skaldship. So the king sent for him,
to come to his court. Thormód set out immediately and approached the king with courtly salutations. The king received
him well and invited him to join his retinue.

"We are told," he said, "that you are well suited to be in
a king's bodyguard and to give your service to princes."

Thormód answered: "I am not suited for that, sire, because I am not able to fill the place of the great skalds who
have been with you before, nor have I as yet attempted to
compose poems on so great a king as you are."

The king said: "Nevertheless it is our will that you remain with us."

Thereupon Thormód answered: "Sire, I am scarcely suited to do so, for I am of a violent disposition, and it might happen—and I would be sorry for it—that I might be so careless as to get into trouble here because of my temperament; for often I am not able to restrain my hot blood. And I pray you will not take amiss what I shall say: it is reported by some that sufficient reward was not given them who did stay with you."

The king said: "Thórarin Praise-Tongue[4] stayed at our court."

Thormód answered: "That is true, sire; yet it did happen at times that he was not sure whether he would get away from here alive. And yet you would find that I am a much poorer skald than is Thórarin."

The king said: "You certainly need much urging, Thormód, and let yourself be asked a long time; but it is nevertheless my will that I require your service."

"May God requite your graciousness, sire," said Thormód; "yet I must be the judge of what is fitting for me, even though I know that it is the greatest honor to serve you."

"Now I shall make it clear," said the king, "as I said before, that all the same it is my wish that you join my company. I shall make you the same conditions as I made to Thórarin, and that was eight ounces of gold."

"Sire!" said Thormód, "if I accept this condition, then I shall greatly require your guidance and counsel; because, as I told you, I have a very short temper indeed."

So Thormód accepted that condition and joined the bodyguard of King Canute. And there he remained for a while and was much honored. He entertained the king frequently (with poems and stories), and it is told that he did that most excellently, and often composed verses on occasion. The king was pleased with him, and yet Thormód got no particular profit from that. Thus the summer passed.

In the following winter, we are told, a man came to court whose name was Hárek. He was a great viking and of a brutal nature, but nevertheless a friend of King Canute, for he was in the habit of bringing him much booty and many precious possessions, and the king valued him highly. We are told that the king asked Hárek how he had fared in summer. He replied that he had not been as lucky as usual, since he had lost his forecastle man.[5]

"And I would request of you, sire, that you furnish me another forecastle man in his place. Yet that will be difficult, it would seem to me, for he was often handy in his speech when that was required, whether for bandying words or for praising men."

The king bethought himself about this matter. He said he would invite Hárek to join his court if he were so minded and quit freebooting, and said it seemed best that he did so. But Hárek said he preferred doing as he was accustomed to. He stayed with the king that winter. He was friendly to Thormód and paid him much courtly attention. Hárek very often talked to the king about the forecastle man he was to furnish him; but the king took his own time about the matter.

Thormód met with little envy on the part of the people at court, as otherwise often is the case with those who are new to it and are shown honors. In the end Hárek told the king that he would choose Thormód to be his forecastle man. The king did not gainsay him, provided that Thormód consented. They brought this matter up to him, but he was by no means eager to accept the offer. At last the king himself took a hand in it and said that it was his will that Thormód joined Hárek.

Thormód answered: "It would suit me best, sire, to remain with you now—I know nothing about this man Hárek."

The king requested Thormód to do as he bid him and promised him his high favor if, this summer at least, he did as he told him to do.

Thormód answered: "I would rather stay with you now, sire; but as you request me to do this I shall not refuse it altogether. However, I wish to make one condition. If I join Hárek on this expedition I want to have the say as to where we shall anchor and where and when to remove."

The king assented to that and said it should be as he wished.

Now when the time approached for Hárek and Thormód to leave court the gifts from the king had not been forthcoming to Thormód which in his opinion had been promised him. And when the king and he happened to be together, Thormód thought it advisable to remind the king of that in some way, and so he spoke this verse:

> 36. Long you gave the lustrous
>   lair-of-Fáfnir[6] to Praise-Tongue—
>   and held out hopes for the
>   hoarded serpent's riches:
>   well, thou far-flung folk-lands'
>   fender, am I from thee
>   worthy reward; or shall I
>   wait for that forever?

At once the king drew from his arm a gold ring weighing four ounces and gave it to Thormód.

"Many thanks, sire," said Thormód, "but be not wroth at my presumption if I say still more about this matter. You said, sire, that I was to receive as pay for my services eight ounces in gold."

The king said: "What you say is true, skald, and I shall not withhold it from you." Then he drew from his arm another ring and gave it to him; and when Thormód received this ring he spoke this verse:

> 37. All can see how in the
>   ample royal court I
>   got the gold-ring-breaker's[7]
>   gifts on both my arms raised;
>   thanks I owe to thane—rich
>   theft-of-Ódin[8] have I—
>   for rings of red gold—sates he
>   ravens—on my arms both.

Thereupon the two parted.

Now Thormód joined Hárek on his ship to be his forecastle man, and they set out on their journey. All the men thought Thormód a man of great ability, both in words and deeds, and they liked him exceedingly well. When summer had nearly passed, so we are told, late one evening they berthed their ship by a certain island. Then they saw some other ships approach close by them. The one heading the fleet was a dragon ship, a magnificent vessel. And when the dragon ship drew near to Thormód's a man called out from the dragon ship: "Out at once, out of the king's harbor!"[9]

The men on board immediately made ready to strike their tents[10] and to remove from that anchorage. But when Thormód saw that he bade them not to remove at all.

"And call to mind now," he said, "it was I who was to decide about such matters."

Then his shipmates answered and begged him not to be so hotheaded though it was true that he had had the decision so far among them and yet might have. Meanwhile the dragon ship shot forward toward their ship and came very close. To those who were aboard the dragon ship it seemed a long while for the other ship to get out of the anchorage. We are told that the forecastle man on the dragon ship stood up and drew his sword and slashed at Thormód; but he was not slow to return the blow, and it so happened that the man got his death from it while Thormód escaped unharmed. And immediately Thormód leaped from his ship onto the dragon ship and, with his shield held before him, ran its whole length back to the poop.[11]

With all this there arose a great outcry, people found out what had happened and Thormód was held; but the vikings made good their escape, not caring what might become of Thormód. It was King Ólaf who was in command of the dragon ship. He was told what had occurred and that the slayer was being held, and he ordered him put to death, saying that he deserved it. But when Finn Árnason[12] heard what the king said he approached and wanted to know who the man was who had killed their forecastle man.

And when the two met he asked: "How is it, man, that you dared to leap on board the king's ship after what you had done?"

Thormód answered: "Because I did not care what would become of me so long as I got into the king's power."

Then Finn told Bishop Sigurd about this and asked him to lend him the power of his intercession with the king to have the man freed. Both thought he had borne himself well. So they prayed the king to let him go and urged his case with great eloquence. The king asked why he had put himself in his power, seeing that he was on the other ship, after what he had done. Thormód overheard him say this and answered the king with this verse:

> 38. All lands my own I'd call if,
> eager steersman bold of
> keel-steeds[13] coursing, thou wouldst
> keep me 'mongst thy followers:
> gladly would I, gallant—
> gory shields we carry—
> wielder-of-the-wound-snake,[14]
> with thee live and die eke!

"Aye," said the king, "it is clear from this exploit of yours that you set little store by your life if only you have your will—and yet I think you would defend well the post given you. What is your name?"

Thormód told him, "and I am the sworn-brother of Thorgeir Hávarsson."

The king said: "You ought to be a man of greater luck than was Thorgeir; but I rather think you are given to mischief, young as you are. How many have you killed already?"

Then Thormód spoke this verse:

> 39. Slain I have now six men
> since that—warrior! often
> stood I in storm-of-arrows[15]—
> started all this un-peace.
> Scarcely is thy skald's age—
> skulls though many crushed I—
> thirty; slain yet saw by
> sword I gold-dispenders.[16]

The king said: "It would be well if you lived not another

thirty years. Yet it is a pity for men like you, as you are likely
to be a great skald."

Thormód answered: "It is now altogether in your power
to determine how old I shall become; but I have hopes of
good things from you because of your friend Thorgeir
Hávarsson, my sworn-brother. And the reason I left Iceland
was chiefly that I thought it certain that you would take
measures to avenge your friend and follower, Thorgeir
Hávarsson. But I considered myself more called on than anyone else to avenge him, with your help and guidance."

The king said: "You shall have your life, seeing you came
to me of your own free will; you can betake yourself wherever you will, so far as I care."

Thormód answered: "Giving me my life means little to
me, because I know no one in Norway; and I will stay with
no king but thee. Now do one thing or another, take me as
your follower or else kill me."

Then, what with the intercession of the bishop and Finn,
and also because the king began to have a liking for Thormód, he said: "Stand up, Thormód, now you will have to
give your life and service to me for the man you slew. You
are well fitted to go on my missions."

Then Thormód spoke this verse:

> 19. Brave must be who long doth
>   bide, king—though thou speakest
>   winsome words to every
>   one—in thy dread presence.
>   Kinsmen few in king's court—
>   cowards none, sire—have I.
>   More is on my mind as
>   my task—loyal to thee.

The king answered: "Your skaldship is likely to afford us
much pleasure; nor do I think that you will be such an unfortunate man after all."

Thormód now stayed with the king, and the king showed
him the more favor the longer he was with him, for Thormód proved himself most courageous in all tests of manhood.

APPENDIX 3 · THORMÓD'S RUSE
AFTER THE BATTLE OF STIKLASTAD

WE ARE told that when the battle was over Thormód went to where Dag and his men had taken their stand after the battle, because there was no longer sufficient daylight for fighting, and night was coming on. The yeomen surrounded Dag and his band to prevent their escape during the night and intended to attack them as soon as daylight permitted.

Dag said: "Is there anyone in my company who can think of a stratagem by which we could escape without the yeomen overpowering us? For I know they will set upon us at dawn if we remain here."

No man raised his voice to answer him.

And when Thormód saw that no one of them had any counsel to offer he said: "Why should not there be a way out?"

Dag asked: "Who is that who spoke so bravely?"

Thormód answered: "My name is Thormód."

Dag said: "Are you Thormód the skald of Coal-Brow?"

"That is who I am," said Thormód.

Dag said: "What plan have you for us to escape with our band?"

Thormód answered: "You are to cut down trees and kindle big fires with the trash and move as many stumps as possible up to the fires. Four men are to be at every fire, with three men constantly moving around it and one keeping it up. And after you have done this for a while, then put out all the fires quickly and at the same time, and make off and stop neither today nor tomorrow. The yeomen will think that a host of men have joined you when they see so many moving around the fires. They will discover our stratagem when morning comes and, I feel sure, will pursue you. But by that time there will be such a distance between you that it will be fruitless."

Dag said: "Are you wounded, perchance, Thormód?"

He answered: "Not at all."

Dag said: "Then come with me east to Sweden and I shall

do what I can for you; for no good can come of your staying here."

Thormód answered: "It is not fated that I shall serve another king, now King Ólaf is fallen."

With that, Thormód turned away. But Dag and his band followed his advice and so escaped.

APPENDIX 4 · VARIANT OF THORMÓD'S DEATH

AFTER this occurrence a woman came into the barn carrying two pails of milk which she intended to give the wounded men to drink. She said to Thormód: "Who is this man standing by the partition?"

Thormód answered: "My name is Thormód."

She said: "Have you perhaps been in the battle today?"

Thormód answered: "I should think that some of the yeomen will have to tell their wives when they get home tonight that Thormód, the skald of Coal-Brow, had joined in the fray today. Yet I rather hope that some will not be able to tell of it."

The woman said: "Which men were foremost in the battle on the side of the king?" Thormód then spoke a verse:

> =33. Eager with open-handed
> Ólaf to fight was Harold;
> by his side, the sword-play
> seeking, Dag and Ring eke:
> stalwart beneath standards
> stood, with red war-shields—
> eagles drank there dead men's
> dark blood—twice twain chieftains.

The woman said: "You seem sorely wounded. Would you drink some milk? That is good for strengthening wounded men."

Thormód answered: "I have no need to drink milk, for I feel sated as if I had just drunk my fill of curdled milk out in Iceland. But I am wounded a little."

The woman said: "Then why are you so pale, if you are not wounded much?"

Then Thormód spoke a verse:

> 40. Ask you why so ashen
>   oak-of-hawk's-land,[17] am I?
>   Few are fain of woundings:
>   flight-of-arrows[18] saw I:
>   strongly sped, the steel-dart
>   stabbed me through the middle;
>   close the cruel iron
>   came to my heart, meseemeth.

The woman said: "I thought I saw by your looks that you were sorely wounded, because you are so pale. Let me bind your wounds as I have done for other men, and let me look at them."

Thormod answered: "I have no need to drink milk, for I feel sated as if I had just drunk my fill of curdled milk in Iceland, but I am wounded a little."

The woman said: "Then why are you so pale, if you are not wounded much?"

Then Thormod spoke a verse:

> 40. Ask you why so ashen
> oak-of-hawk's-land" am I?
> Few are fain of woundings:
> flight-of-arrows" saw I:
> strongly sped, the steel-dart
> stabbed me through the middle;
> close the cruel iron
> came to my heart, meseemeth.

The woman said: "I thought I saw by your looks that you were sorely wounded, because you are so pale. For the bind your wounds as I have done for other men, and let me look at them."

NOTES

NOTES ON KORMÁK'S SAGA

CHAPTER I. KORMÁK'S PARENTAGE

1. He ruled ca. 860-930.

2. A name borne by many high-born and distinguished Irishmen. Since his grandsons, Fródi and Thorgils, have names identical with those of the chieftains who founded a Norwegian kingdom in Dublin, and since the skald's mother was called Dalla, which very likely also is Irish, it is safe to assume kinship with some chieftains in Ireland. Typical Irish traits are easily discernible in the skald's appearance and temperament.

3. District around the Oslo Fiord. Like most pre-settlement accounts in the family sagas, the story of Ogmund's youthful exploits and first marriage probably is fictitious.

4. About the holmgang and its rules, see the *locus classicus*, Chap. X.

CHAPTER II. OGMUND SETTLES IN ICELAND

1. He ruled ca. 930-945. His mother Gunnhild early acquired the reputation of being a sorceress. Reading between the lines, we may trace her ill will pursuing Ogmund in the death of Helga and her son and in the declining fortunes of the family.

2. They represent the lares and penates of the Old Norse household. Their indwelling divinity chooses the location of the new homestead.

3. Both Skeggi and his sword Skofnung figure importantly in a number of sagas. He is credited with taking it out of the tumulus of the legendary King Hrólf Kraki.

4. This belief seems unknown otherwise.

5. Elsewhere, to be sure, his complexion is described as sallow.

CHAPTER III. KORMÁK FALLS IN LOVE WITH STEINGERD

1. The women occupied separate quarters during the day for plying their handiwork.

2. The "hall" (*skáli*) served as general living room but had also arrangements for eating and sleeping. Cf. p. 89, note 2.

3. Unfortunately, in this passage as in others following, the description in the saga is peculiarly unsatisfactory for giving an idea of the situation.

4. Frigg is Ódin's wife; the whole, a kenning for "woman." In the Icelandic "hall" there was a dark passageway running between the outer wall of stones and turf and the inner wall of timber.

5. "Hagbard's beard (head)" probably referred to the carved doorposts representing figures from myth or legend. Hagbard was the young hero whose love for Signe is immortalized by Saxo Grammaticus and in the Danish ballad. However, for certain reasons the translator holds that the figure represented was that of Hárbard (Ódin). In neither case must we look upon it as a symbol of erotic significance.

6. I.e., "her eyes."

7. Kenning for "eyes."

8. A goddess; the whole, a kenning for "woman."

9. This stanza is attributed, but with less probability, also to the skald Gunnlaug.

10. A difficult stanza, translated *ad sensum.*

11. The "land" (i.e., support) of the (hunting) hawk is the arm; its Hlín (a name of the goddess Frigg) is the lady.

12. Kenning for "woman."

13. Ilm is a goddess; the whole, a kenning for "woman."

14. I.e., "great hundreds" (120) ells of wadmal (homespun), which was a common measure of value.

15. Kenning for "woman."

16. One cannot be sure whether the semi-mythical land of the Huns or Germany is meant.

17. The goddess of fertility; the whole, a kenning for "woman."

18. The long silver needle, shaped like an arrow, used for holding the braids.

19. A goddess; the whole, a kenning for "woman."

Chapter IV. Kormák Punishes Narfi

1. A bizarre kenning for "sausage." Narfi is taunting Kormák as being a person too much interested in the affairs of the kitchen.

2. These improvised lines are somewhat along the scheme of the *hnugghent* meter (with 7 syllables in lines 1 and 3); cf. *Snorra Edda, Háttatal* 76.

3. A divinity (following the emendation of Jon Thórkelsson); the whole, a kenning for "rustic."

4. From the kitchen smoke.

5. A scornful kenning for "slave."

Chapter V. Kormák Slays Thórveig's Sons. Her Curse

1. It was located north of Mel.

2. The elevated platform at the gable end of the hall was reserved for the women.

3. Kenning for "shield." The giant Hrungnir, when warned that his opponent, Thór, was coming at him from below the earth, stood on his shield.

4. A kenning for "woman."

5. I.e., the art of skaldship. Ódin stole "the mead of poetry" from the giants and gave of it to the skalds.

6. The second helming offers difficulties that have not as yet been solved satisfactorily; hence the translation is largely guesswork.

7. I.e., glances of the eye.

8. Viz., in ambush.

9. Kennings for "woman." Gná and Gefn are goddesses.

10. The versification of this stanza in the original approaches the *dunhent* measure family of *dróttkvætt*. Cf. *Háttatal* 53.

Chapter VI. Kormák Wins Steingerd's Hand but Fails to Appear at the Marriage

1. Kenning for "battle."

2. Though with hesitations, I have followed Moebius in the interpretation of lines 3 and 4 of this difficult helming. The stanza, a variation of 18, does not fit the context as the sons of Thórveig have already been slain.

3. Kenning for "woman."

4. At least, this seems the meaning of these difficult lines.

5. I.e., Kormák; cf. Chap. II.

6. Kenning for "generous man, prince": the prince rewards his warriors with pieces of golden arm rings.

7. The same holds as for note 4 above.

Chapter VII. Steingerd Is Married Off to Bersi

1. Bersi is a historic personage mentioned also in the *Laxdæla saga*, but nothing is known otherwise about his wife, his sister, or his son.

2. It is a neighborhood, rather, in one of the best farming districts of Western Iceland. Bersi himself lived on the farm called after him, Bessatunga.

3. In the same neighborhood.

4. These personages are mentioned also in other sagas.

5. Very probably this is an error. There is, however, a farm called Hvol in Saurbær; its location fits circumstances much better.

6. Most likely a fictitious personage.

7. A rammer is a device for driving or compacting something—here, to ram fast the sods on the outer walls of an Icelandic house.

8. The whole sentence is curiously confused. If one may read between the lines of the poorly told episode, it would seem that Kormák does not immediately grasp the full import of what Narfi tells him or that he thought Narfi was mocking him with some malicious make-belief.

9. Mock-heroic kenning for "hero": breaking into the tumulus erected over a dead chieftain—in order to rob him of the sword and treasure buried with him—was a deed of daring, because it was thought to involve a struggle for life and death with his ghost.

Chapter VIII. Kormák Vainly Pursues Bersi

1. The skald (Kormák), who as such is befriended by Ygg (Ódin).

2. The meaning of this curious helming, elliptic also in the original, seems to be that, like the bat lying by the well, ready to be used for beating the wash, the poet is everlastingly ready to celebrate Steingerd in song.

3. It has seemed best, following Finnur Jónsson, to separate these two facetious helmings; of which, for that matter, only the second has any bearing on the narrative here.

4. An exceedingly difficult and ill-understood helming.

Chapter IX. Kormák Borrows the Sword Skofnung

1. She occurs also in some other sagas as a witch.

2. This locality is still pointed out in the mouth of the Hvolsá and Stadarholtsá creeks. The Tialdaness promontory is close by.

3. Kennings for "woman."

4. Similar amulets occur frequently in the *Fornaldarsǫgur* (the Tales of Marvel in the Olden Times).

5. The sword Skofnung plays a role also in the *Laxdœla saga*. As to a serpent lying hidden in the hilt (see page 32), possibly the notion may have arisen with oriental swords from Damascus in which a wavy pattern is etched that in certain lights has a serpentine motion.

6. It is a well-known belief that favorite tools and arms come to partake of the nature of the owner.

CHAPTER X. THE HOLMGANG BETWEEN KORMÁK AND BERSI

1. Nothing is known from other sources about there being any difference between the *einvígi* (single combat) and the holmgang.

2. In all likelihood, these had phallic shape and, as such, a consecrating or prophylactic power; just as the manner in which they were to be approached was connected with the "evil eye" and the prevention of its influence.

3. Or, rather, poles, made of hazelwood, which had magic property.

CHAPTER XI. KORMÁK ENGAGES STEINAR'S HELP AND RETURNS SKOFNUNG

1. A historic figure who occurs also in other sagas. His farm Ellidi lies on the Snæfellsness peninsula.

2. Kennings for "warrior": Ullr and Baldr are divinities.

3. Referring to the map, one can see how vague the author's notions of topography are.

4. I.e., with the healing-stone.

5. Hild is a valkyrie; her "storm," hence, is a kenning for "battle."

6. I.e., the cloak (of hide) on which the holmgang is fought.

7. I.e., Bersi's party. The last two lines of the stanza are difficult. I follow Finnur Jónsson's (to be sure, violent) emendation *sigr varða þá*, etc., because it allows a translation more fitting the connection: it was not his, but the sword's, fault that he lost.

8. Bersi is the (tabu) name for "bear"; the whole, a playful kenning for "warrior" and Bersi in particular.

9. Kenning for "sword."

10. I.e., probably, Steingerd.

11. Kenning for "sword" as striking sparks from the iron-rimmed shield.

12. The helming is difficult; yet so much is clear that the skald here carries through the figure of Skofnung grudgingly leaving its sheath like a bear issuing growling out of its den.

13. Kennings for "woman."

14. The occurrences here alluded to have no counterpart in the prose; hence the interpretation of the stanza as here given is purely conjectural.

15. Frey is the god of fertility; the whole, a kenning for warrior.

CHAPTER XII. BERSI FALLS OUT WITH THÓRD AND IS CHALLENGED BY STEINAR

1. The usual game was the *knáttleikr*, which in some respects resembled lacrosse.

2. Bork plays an important, and mostly odious, role in a number of sagas, especially the *Gísla saga*.

2a. Or, "it is not said that because you are indigent I should lose my money." In either case, an insult is meant—about as if we should say: "Now you are begging, but I won't let you go to the poorhouse."

3. On the north side of the Snæfellsness peninsula.

4. I.e., the Hvammsfirth.

5. A famous farm, not far from Saurbær, prominently figuring in the *Laxdœla saga*.

6. I.e., space for sitting and also for spreading one's bedding.

7. Both names suggest a gloomy, sinister appearance.

8. Bersi anticipates Steinar's aim to provoke him by occupying his customary place during the thing.

9. "The gale-of-arrows" is a kenning for "battle"; its "urger," a warrior.

10. I.e., on the corpses of the slain: kenning for "warrior."

11. The second helming has not as yet been satisfactorily explained so that the translation is largely guesswork.

12. The measure of this stanza is *fornyrthislag*, the epic measure, with two stresses to the line.

13. Both the bag stuffed with aromatic herbs and the hose had magic properties. The moss from a dead man's skull protected against weapons; hence also its color had this property. Note that, robbed of these magic possessions, Bersi loses his invulnerability and heals slowly.

14. It is mentioned also in the *Egils saga*.

15. Kenning for "warrior."

16. Kenning for "valkyrie."

17. Kenning for "warrior."

18. The interpretation of the helming is doubtful; perhaps it means: even though you do not, the valkyrie will help me.

19. Hlokk is a valkyrie; the whole, a kenning for "battle."

20. His father had lived in the Borgarthing district, south of Saurbær. The translator pleads for indulgence for the irregularity of the line—paralleled though by some of Bersi's—as it did not prove feasible to compress the substance of the helming otherwise.

21. Used here in the sense of "threats."

22. Bestla is the giantess mother of Odin, who has the mead of poetry, stolen from the giants, in his keeping; the whole, a kenning for "skald."

Chapter XIII. Steingerd Divorces Bersi

1. Ygg is one of Óðin's names; the whole, a kenning for "man."

2. While clear on the whole, the stanza offers difficulties, and its translation is, therefore, *ad sensum*.

3. In the pre-Christian time, a divorce was easily obtained in the North by simply declaring one's intention before witnesses. The consent of the other party was not essential.

4. More accurately, east.

5. This is the gift, of stipulated value, made to the woman by the husband on the morning after the marriage.

Chapter XIV. Bersi Slays Thorkel

1. Scil. In that he loses his wife and they, her property.

2. Cf. note 2, p. 30.

2a. This is probably the meaning of *ték tanna*—whether in glee or in defiance.

3. Ullr is a god; the whole, a kenning for "warrior" (Bersi himself).

4. The second helming is difficult, both as to details and general meaning. In the interpretation here given, the reference is to the heathen belief that Óðin's host in the final conflict with the powers of destruction is augmented by warriors slain in battle.

5. The stanza is a variation of 37.

6. A farm not far from Bersi's.

CHAPTER XV. BERSI RESCUES STEINVOR AND KILLS THÓRARIN AND HIS SONS

1. He and his sons are unknown otherwise, but his father occurs in the *Eyrbyggja saga.*

2. Cf. p. 89, note 2.

3. Kålund has no discussion of where this may be, but very possibly it is confused with the locale in which Váli is slain.

CHAPTER XVI. BERSI KILLS VÁLI

1. Kenning for "warrior."

2. Cf. p. 86, note 5.

3. I.e., ravens, as scavengers of the battle field.

4. The same stanza occurs also in the *Laxdœla saga* (Chap. 18) where, however, it is better motivated, in Halldór's still being an infant one year old who is spilled from his cradle and lies helplessly on the floor while Bersi on account of sickness can only look on. The measure is *fornyrthislag,* with the last four lines rhyming.

5. Probably not to be taken literally but rather indicating infirmity.

6. Kenning for "sword."

7. Kenning for "warrior."

8. It is difficult to see why Váli should be interested to see justice done to Steinvor against his own sister.

9. As to the location of this defile, cf. the discussion of Kålund, *Bidrag til en historisk-topografisk Beskrivelse af Island,* I, 500-501.

10. Also, where the corpse was to be found. Without these proceedings the slaying would be accounted murder.

CHAPTER XVII. STEINGERD MARRIES THORVALD

1. The name is Celtic. Cf. Cornish *tin-tan* "the lower fortress"; or else *tin-den* "the castle on the hill." Kormák uses it for convenient puns, cf. p. 55, note 9.

1a. As a fact, these personages belonged to an important clan which claimed many distinguished persons. Fliót is on the northeastern shore of the Skagafirth; Svínavatn (where Thorvald lived), south of it.

2. A considerable journey, hardly to be accomplished in less than a day's riding.

3. Or rather, kirtle. It was customary in many countries for the bride to sew one for the groom as a symbol of the intimate relations they were entering on.

4. Nanna is Baldr's wife; the whole, a kenning for "woman."

Chapter XVIII. Kormák and Thorgils in Viking Raids Abroad

1. She is trying to exert the power of "the evil eye" on him. It was common belief that witches could "send out their souls" in the shape of animals to harm their enemies. Their eyes would stay unchanged during the transformation.

2. (?)945-961.

3. In the harbor, parts of the ship were tented over at night for protection against the elements.

4. Alliteration and the choice of words in the original suggest that this reply may be the fragment of a stanza now lost.

Chapter XIX. Kormák Fights in King Harold's Expeditions. Kormák Returns to Iceland and Encounters Steingerd

1. He ruled 961-970.

2. This evidently is a nickname of Thorgils.

3. A skerry is a partly submerged rock or reef; its "land," the sea; and the "tree of that land," a (rather unusual) kenning for "woman."

4. Sif is Thór's wife; the whole, a kenning for "woman."

5. Haki is a typical viking name, so "Haki's-blue-land," the sea. Its "steep slopes" are the breakers on its "strands," i.e., the beaches (from the point of view of the land). As to kennings of this complex nature, cf. Hollander, *The Skalds*, p. 13.

6. Outside the Sognefjord (Norway).

7. Kenning for "ship."

8. Kenning for "men."

9. In the original there is a play on Tintein's name, which is changed into (es) *tin tannar* "he who chews tin."

10. Kenning for "woman."

11. Most likely the poet has in mind the phosphorescence of the sea.

12. As to the improbability of their meeting here, cf. p. 50, note 2.

13. Kennings for "woman."

14. Kennings for "woman."

15. The translation is *ad sensum* as the stanza seems hopelessly corrupt.

16. Similar figures for the "reversal of nature" from classic and modern literature will readily come to mind.

17. Kennings for "woman."

18. I.e., he is haunted by ill fortune; at least such is the translator's interpretation of this difficult passage.

19. Meant ironically, of course.

Chapter XX. Kormák Is Slandered

1. Actually, more east than north.

2. Thrúd is Thór's daughter; the whole, a kenning for "woman."

3. The words of the original—* stands for a syllable omitted—have resisted interpretation, but no doubt contain some obscenity. For the rest I have accepted Finnur Jónsson's emendations, especially of *stœdilát* (fem. adj.) for *stœrilát*.

Chapter XXI. Thorvard Challenges Kormák but Fails to Come to the Single Combat

1. Kenning for "warrior," meant ironically.

2. The scornful reference is to the mythological giant Mokkurkálfi who was to assist Hrungnir in the battle against Thór and whose heart was of clay.

3. I.e., Thorvald.

4. Gaut is one of Ódin's names; the whole, a kenning for skaldship.

5. I.e., such lampooning verses as the foregoing one.

6. The stanza is difficult and capable of various interpretations.

7. It was held at Thingeyrar, on the southern shore of the Húnafirth.

Chapter XXII. Kormák's Visit to the Sorceress Thórdís. He Lames Thorvard

1. The goose was, to be sure, a sacrificial animal among the ancients, parts of it having been used for medicinal and pro-

phylactic purposes; but the slaughtering of the animal for love magic is not attested elsewhere.

2. Scil. of Ódin; i.e., the art of skaldship.

3. The translation of this difficult stanza is conjectural. The poet appears indignant that he, a friend of Ódin, shall owe his life to two ganders slaughtered.

4. This seems a technical term for "aided by magic."

5. Cf. the Eddic *Hǫvamǫl*, st. 131: "be most wary of all / of other man's wife." A warning to Thorvard?

6. Kenning for "battle."

7. Witches can be recognized by the peculiar quality of their eyes. Their glance can devastate nature. But it is not clear why, in this instance, Kormák wants to drag Thórdís out into the sunlight as he already has sufficient proof that she is a witch.

8. Kenning for "woman."

9. As the narrator later (after stanza 74) informs us, this was a customary sacrifice after the holmgang. From what follows it appears that Kormák neglected to redden the "elves' hill" with the blood of the bull.

10. Kenning for "woman."

11. Kenning for "sword."

12. A gesture symbolic of familiarity, it seems.

13. Kenning for "woman."

14. A difficult stanza, translated *ad sensum*.

CHAPTER XXIII. THORVARD DUELS WITH KORMÁK AGAIN AND IS INCAPACITATED

1. (Scornful) kenning for "warrior."

2. Fiolnir is one of Ódin's names; the whole, a kenning for "poetry."

3. Kenning for "sword" (as biting the shield).

CHAPTER XXIV. KORMÁK AS WELL AS STEINGERD AND THORVALD SAIL TO NORWAY

1. I.e., Thorvard, for losing twice in the holmgang.

2. Kenning for "woman."

3. Kenning for "woman."

4. I.e., the single street of which the king's residence (at Drontheim) consisted then.

CHAPTER XXV. KORMÁK FELLS THORVALD ON AN EXPEDITION WITH KING HAROLD

1. This took place about A.D. 964.
2. This stanza is of doubtful authenticity.
3. Such were used (instead of a clasp or buckle) to hold the cloak together.
4. A pun seems intended in the original, "deila" meaning both "to deal, share, divide into parts" and "to fall out about something."

CHAPTER XXVI. KORMÁK RESCUES STEINGERD FROM VIKINGS

1. Situated at the mouth of the Göta Elf.
2. In the original, "married to a man," viz., as a prize.
3. Sea creatures of some kind, real or imaginary—possibly sent out by Thórveig's magic to drown Kormák.
4. Kenning for "woman."
5. The second helming, though technically perfect, is much of a puzzle; the rendering of it, therefore, purely conjectural.
6. Gerd is a giantess, the wife of Freyr; the whole, a kenning for "woman."
7. Kenning for "woman."
8. Kenning for "poetry"; i.e. Kormák's verses to her.

CHAPTER XXVII. KORMÁK FALLS IN SCOTLAND

1. On the coast of York. As the name shows it was founded by one Skarthi.
2. Just what is meant by the *blótrisi* of the original is hard to say.
3. Cf. p. 44, note 4.
4. From this it would seem that Skrýmir had rather leaped out of its scabbard to help Kormák and that there is some misunderstanding of the verse.
5. Kenning for "woman."
6. Kenning for "sword."
7. Sága is one of the goddess Frigg's names; the whole, a kenning for "woman."
8. A kenning for "blood."
9. A kenning for "warriors."

NOTES ON
THE SWORN BROTHERS' SAGA

CHAPTER I. THORBIORG SAVES GRETTIR FROM THE NOOSE

1. The missionary king of Norway (995-1030). He was canonized in 1031, after an eclipse of the sun and when many miracles had been attributed to his remains.

2. Passages bracketed are clearly interpolated; cf. Introduction, p. 81.

3. "And" is lacking in all MSS except *R*, which would make Thorgrím the brother of Víga-Styr. The correct relation is set forth in the *Heiðarvíga saga*, Chap. 3; where we learn also that Vermund was called *inn mjóvi* (the Slender).

4. Grettir the Strong, the famous outlaw about whom there exists the full-length biography of the *Grettis saga*. The same story is told there (Chap. 52) at greater length. As to the verse (in the measure called *kviðuháttr*, cf. *The Skalds*, 76) here attributed to Grettir, it is probably not genuine, though it may be old. It forms stanza 6 of the so-called "Lay about his Life" incorporated in the *Grettis saga*.

5. Once the sentence of the (greater) outlawry was imposed on a man, anyone had the right to kill him—if he could. As the executive branch was lacking in Iceland, the carrying out of the sentence devolved on the injured party; but the person sentenced often escaped by flight or the protection given by powerful kinsmen.

CHAPTER II. THORGEIR AND THORMÓD AND THEIR KINSFOLK. JODUR KILLS THORGEIR'S FATHER

1. This must be a mistake. The farm Dyrðilmýri lies far away, on the north shore of the Ice Firth, which would have precluded a close early friendship. See Kålund, *op.cit.*, 1, 596.

2. As in the case of so many Icelandic skalds, there seems to have been some admixture of Celtic blood in Thormód. He also stammered, cf. p. 154.

3. Even now, Reykiahólar is one of the best farms in that part of Iceland. Its name "Smoke Heights" derives from the presence of steaming springs on the small peninsula of Reykianess.

4. With these progenitors' names we enter the realm of myth on either side.

5. Thenceforward they are *svaribræðr*, "sworn-brothers." This passage is the *locus classicus*—beside the one in the *Gísla-saga*. Chap. 6—for the rites of blood-brothership between men. It is to be distinguished from true foster-brothership (as exemplified in the case of Thorgeir Spendthrift and Eyolf, Chap. 19), where children, often related, were brought up by foster-parents as *fóstbræðr*, "foster-brothers."

6. Actually, in a northerly direction; but what is meant is, in the general direction of the West Firths.

7. As the name (Acreness) indicates, grain was formerly grown there. At present no grain is profitably grown in Iceland.

8. This curious bit of physiology, half Germanic, half classic, is unique in Old Norse literature.

CHAPTER III. THORGEIR AVENGES HIS FATHER'S DEATH. THORGEIR AND THORMÓD WITH THE WIDOW SIGRFLIÓD

1. A euphemistic idiom for "to be slain," much favored by the author.

2. It was the custom for the farm folk of Old Iceland to assemble in the kitchen (*eldhús*) about the fire so soon as outside work had to stop on account of the darkness, and then to adjourn to the contiguous *stofa*. This room, here inadequately translated by "living room," served both as a dining room and a general sitting and work room.

3. "Ready for Battle."

4. This is a longer encomiastic poem whose stanzas are generally held together by a refrain. Cf. *The Skalds*, p. 10.

5. A kenning for "ship."

6. I.e., the outer door. It opens into a hallway between *stofa* and the *skali* in which all the inmates of the farm slept.

7. Cf. p. 86, note 6.

8. I.e., westward from the head of the firth.

9. Again, the general direction is intended. He stays with Thormód at Laugaból.

10. The use of *eiðr* in this sense is not instanced in the dictionaries.

11. See p. 103, note 1.

12. Rán is the goddess of the sea; her daughters, the waves. This mythologic incursion into the prose is probably unique in Old Norse literature. Cf. also the bracketed passage on p. 95.

13. I.e., whether friend or foe.

CHAPTER IV. THEY ATTACK INGOLF AND THORBRAND

1. This is the first office of hospitality in Iceland even now.

2. A misunderstood kenning: *Elri* signifies "the alder tree," its dog (or destroyer), "fire"; cf. Sveinbjǫrn Egilsson, *Lexicon Poëticum Antiquæ Linguæ Septentrionalis*, p. 134. But here, of course, the wind is meant.

3. However, to reach the Horn Strands (cf. p. 103, note 1) overland from here at this time of the year, over the difficult mountains filling the peninsula, would have been well nigh impossible. Also, it would have been hard to bring away any whale meat found.

CHAPTER V. INGOLF AND THORBRAND ARE SLAIN. SIGRFLIÓD PACIFIES VERMUND

1. Kennings for "ships." Their ruler or steersman, "sailor, warrior."

CHAPTER VI. THORGEIR SLAYS BUTRALDI

1. The description makes it uncertain whether the *stofa* or the *skáli* is meant.

2. As in Scotland, an elevated plateau was in Iceland called a heath. They would have to cross the high lands separating the Ice Firth from the Skjálmar Firth in the south. Cf. Kålund, *op.cit.* I, 600. The following description shows an accurate knowledge of this route.

3. It reminds one of Skarphedin's famous exploit on the ice-floe in the Markar River, *Njáls saga*, Chap. 92.

4. I.e., "the battle."

5. Cf. p. 88, note 1.

CHAPTER VII. THE FIGHT OVER THE WHALE. THORGEIR AND THORMÓD PART COMPANY

1. I.e., the Horn Strands—stretches of shore line east and west of Cape Horn (i.e., corner). The "common lands" (*almenningar*) there, in particular, form two sections which were not privately owned but were free for all and were frequently visited because they offer a wealth of driftwood and occasional stranded whales. Finders were keepers, but had to be prepared to defend their prizes against others. Cf. Kålund, *op.cit.* I, 413f.

2. This whole episode is told similarly but more briefly in the

Grettis saga, Chap. 25. But the following lawsuit, which ends with Thorgeir's being outlawed, is given there in greater detail (Chaps. 26, 27) although it is not organic there.

3. From this stanza it would seem that their disagreement was originally caused by "slander sowed" between them. The *Flatey-arbók* version (II, 105) has the following about their parting (the scene is laid in the Gils Firth, with the two sworn-brothers riding on the beach beneath the sea-cliff Drífandi) : At that moment Thorgeir rode forward past the cliff. The flood tide had come in so that his horse was about to have to swim under him; and when he had passed the fording place beneath the cliff he leaped from his horse and saw that Thormód had turned his horse toward the mouth of the firth—probably not wishing to imitate Thorgeir's feat. He shouted to Thormód to ride past the cliff also; but Thormód answered: "We shall now have to part for the present—fare you well!" and rode along the shore toward the mouth of the Gils Firth and did not stop till he arrived home at Laugaból. For the location, cf. Kålund, *op.cit.* I, 505f.

Chapter VIII. Biarni Appropriates Thorgeir's Horse and Is Slain by Him. Thorgeir Sails to Norway and Joins King Ólaf's Bodyguard

1. I.e., in this case the Althing, held on the *Thingvellir* (Thing Plain) in the southwestern part of the island. To get there, parties from the west and northwest had to cross the numerous valleys of the Dales District, where dwelled Thorstein Kuggason, one of Thorgils Mársson's kinsmen, who was most active in pushing the prosecution of Thorgeir. According to the account of the *Grettis saga*, Chap. 27, Thorgils Arason, Thorgeir's kinsman and protector, was only lukewarm in his cause. After all, a good defence could have been made, in that all men could partake in the catch on the common lands, and Thorgils had accepted Thorgeir's challenge and was slain in open battle. As to the former point, however, the law-speaker, who was related to Ásmund, the other prosecutor, ruled that settled farmers had preferential right as against single persons. Thereupon Thorgils Arason gives up the case—he may have been glad to be rid of his troublesome nephew!

2. So that it would not have been profitable to prosecute him anew.

3. Kenning for "ships."

4. This is in flat contradiction to what was stated above and the detailed account of the *Grettis saga*; moreover it is highly unlikely, as Thorgeir leaves the country because of the verdict. But Thormód was acquitted against payment of a fine: possibly their names are confused here.

5. The above rather pointless episode smacks of the *Fornaldarsǫgur* style and seems purely fictitious.

6. These stanzas, then, were evidently lost by the time the saga was composed.

7. Present-day Pomerania.

8. Its mouth, unlike that of most of Iceland's rivers, is navigable for small ships. The other topographic names exist no longer. Cf. Kålund, *op.cit.* 1, 363.

9. Kenning for "ship."

10. "Wound serpent" is a kenning for "sword"; its wielder, then, is a warrior.

11. Kenning for "ship."

12. Following F. Jónsson, as against Kock's reading, *Notationes Norrœnæ*, 690.

Chapter IX. Thormód Falls in Love with Thordís. He Is Wounded by Kolbak

1. Cf. Kålund, *op.cit.* 1, 593f., for a discussion of some minor discrepancies in the account given here of the locale of the following episodes. Interesting enough, the great *Hauksbók* MS. was first discovered here by the learned Arngrím Jónsson (about 1600).

2. A word *vindr* (fem. cons. stem) of this meaning is not instanced in any dictionary. It is connected with *vinda*, "to wind," *vinda* fem. "hank of yarn."

3. "The fire-of-the flood" is a kenning for "gold"—from the Niflung gold hidden in the Rhine; its dispenser, therefore, is a "(generous) man."

Chapter X. Bersi Vainly Seeks Kolbak. Gríma Helps Kolbak Leave Iceland

1. The "lower bench," opposite the seat of honor in the living room, is occupied by the farm hands.

2. There is a pun here. The Old Norse *heilsa* meant "to salute one with hail (health, good fortune)" and then, weakened, "to greet."

Chapter XI. Thormód Composes the Coal-Brow Ditties

1. This settlement near the mouth of the Ice Firth even now is a considerable fishing village.

2. Thrúd is a goddess, the daughter of Thór. A kenning for "woman."

Chapter XII. Thorgeir Slays Snorri

1. He is apparently the son of one Hœkil ("Bent-Knee").

2. A slaying had to be reported at once by the perpetrator at the nearest dwelling or else it was considered a murder. This information was often conveyed in veiled or, as here, ironic, terms so as to allow the slayer to escape.

3. *Hvítr* in Old Norse meant, not only "white, light-blond," but also "cowardly"; cf. our "white-livered." For that matter, his opponent, Thorstein Egilsson, also was noted for his light-colored hair. Cf. *Egils saga*, Chapter 79, where other boundary quarrels about the same land are told in organic connection. The episode here told is totally unrelated to the saga.

Chapter XIII. Thorgeir Slays Thórir. Veglág's Thefts. Thorgeir Joins the Orkney Earl

1. Scil., with the timber he had brought from Norway.

2. The outside walls of an Icelandic house were made of turf and stones, with a narrow passageway between the outside wall and the inside planking.

3. He held office from 1216 to 1236 and was consecrated in 1233. The *Hauksbók* version of the saga relates that the hall was 19 by 40 ells and was still standing when the second Bishop Arni was consecrated (1304) at Skálholt; which change no doubt is due to Hauk himself.

4. Kenning for "(generous) man." Odd is the name of King Ólaf's man.

5. In Old Norse law the punishment for theft was death (as was legally the case in England till 1828). This could be inflicted on a serf without process of law.

6. This is clearly a mistake since Laugaból is directly north of Reykianess.

7. At this place the *Flateyarbók* narrative (II, 159) inserts the story of the adventure on the cliff (see Appendix I, p. 179), as though there had been a reconciliation.

8. The *Orkneyinga saga* (Chap. 17) tells us that Rognvald was only ten years old when taken by his father Brúsi to the court of King Ólaf in 1021 (cf. Taylor, ed., 159). As the expedition here referred to must have taken place at least 5 years before Ólaf went into exile (1028), it would seem to have been headed by Brúsi. Later, Rognvald fought at the king's side at Stiklastad and helped Harold, the king's half-brother, to escape (cf. p. 174, note 25).

9. Kenning for "ship."

CHAPTER XIV. THORGEIR'S LAST STAY WITH KING ÓLAF

1. Like so many kings in Old Norse literature, King Ólaf is endowed with divinatory powers.

2. Actually, he traveled almost directly west, as is also stated below.

3. This nickname probably refers to a cryptorchid condition.

CHAPTER XV. THE FOSTER-BROTHERS EYÓLF AND THORGEIR SPENDTHRIFT. THORGEIR HÁVARSSON SLAYS GAUT

1. More properly, east.

2. This comes closer, I believe, to the spirit of the riming proverb (*svá er leikr hverr sem heiman er gerr*) than Finnur Jónsson's translation (*Arkiv för nordisk Filologi* 1914, p. 107, no. 245) "saaledes er leg som den er hjemme forberedt."

CHAPTER XVI. THORGRÍM AND THÓRARIN PLAN TO OVERCOME THORGEIR HÁVARSSON

1. About him there exists a short *þáttr* (story) appended to the *Ljósvetninga saga*. It tells about the following battle in about the same way but more sketchily.

CHAPTER XVII. THORGEIR HÁVARSSON'S FALL

1. Kenning for "ship."

2. Kennings for "warrior."

3. Gull-of-combat is a kenning for "raven" or "eagle"; its feeder, "a warrior."

CHAPTER XVIII. THORMÓD BECOMES KING ÓLAF'S MAN

1. According to the *þórarins þáttr* (see above, p. 134, note 1) he salted the head down and had it with him to the Althing, where

he showed it to prove his claim for the prize set on it. He then buried it near his home by the Island Firth. Hearing of the slaying of his follower Thorgeir, King Ólaf sent money to induce Gudmund's son, Eyólf, to kill Thórarin.

2. More likely, they feared the consequences of robbing the property of the powerful Reykiahólar clan. For the same reason, Kálf and Steinólf may have been spared.

3. At this point the *Flateyarbók* ii, 199, has the account, stirring but of dubious authenticity, of how Thormód joined the court of King Ólaf. See Appendix 2, p. 180.

4. According to the *Hauksbók* version, Thórarin Arrogance was made an outlaw together with the others who had participated in the battle; and Gudmund the Powerful, a rich chieftain of the Northern Quarter, had a hand in the subsequent killing of Thórarin, for which he was paid as told here.

5. That is, the Snæfellsjǫkul (the glacier-covered mountain at the extremity of the Snæfell peninsula separating the Broad Firth from the Faxa Firth). This route would bring the travelers appreciably nearer to their homes at Ólafsdale.

6. This is the place of assemblage for the crew on shipboard.

CHAPTER XX. THORMÓD AND GEST SAIL FOR GREENLAND

1. He means, ironically, by main force.

2. There is a pun here in the original, *yrkja* meaning both "to work" and "to compose poetry."

3. In the so-called *Eystri Bygð* (Eastern Settlement) of Greenland.

4. He is a son of Leif Eriksson who discovered America and introduced Christianity into Greenland.

5. It was the prerogative of the chief of a district to have first choice of the wares brought by ships from abroad; also, to fix values in the exchange for native goods.

CHAPTER XXI. THORMÓD QUARRELS WITH LODIN

1. The (inheritable) office of *goði* belonged to the most influential man of a district. He presided at juridical and religious functions.

2. These lines are part of the Eddic *Hǫvamǫl*, stanza 84.

CHAPTER XXII. THORMÓD SLAYS LODIN

1. In larger houses the dais (*flet*) paralleled the long side of the hall.

2. Nothing is known about this game.

CHAPTER XXIII. THORMÓD AVENGES THORGEIR ON THORGRÍM.
HE SLAYS THORGRÍM'S SONS. GRÍMA CONCEALS THORMÓD
FROM THORDÍS

1. The cheaper axes had a steel edge annealed into the iron of the blade. The weal at the juncture naturally interfered with the cutting quality of the weapon; nor was such a weapon quite trustworthy. Cf. Hjalmar Falk, *Altnordische Waffenkunde*, p. 107.

2. These semi-permanent booths had turf or stone walls, but the roofs consisted of hides or other materials stretched over rafters.

3. Kenning for "warrior."

4. The bearing of the line so translated here is not clear.

5. I.e., King Ólaf.

6. This passage has often been quoted as illustrative of the circumstances of saga telling and writing.

7. *Ótryggr*, "untrustworthy"—which occurs as the name of persons. *Tortryggr*, "not safe to trust."

8. Here the *Flateyarbók* version, II, 211, inserts the droll anatomic information that for fear all his bones shook (214 of them); his teeth rattled (30 in number); and all his veins trembled (of which there are 415); and it has a stanza of manifestly late manufacture.

9. "Eager for Battle."

10. The original has the equivalent vulgarism, *ǫll es fremð fallin í strá greppi.*

11. "Sword-storm" is a kenning for "battle"; its "urger," therefore, "a chieftain." Similarly the "storm-of-steel's impellers," below.

12. Kenning for "gold"; its dispenser is "the (generous) chieftain."

13. I.e., by fate.

14. Instead of the following words of Thormód, the *Flateyarbók* version, II, 165, has the following: Skúf said: "Very possibly; but was not Falgeir present, the son of Thordís, that big fighter?"

Thormód answered: "He was."

Skúf said: "Then he will probably be furious about the slaying of his kinsman Thorgrím."

Thormód spoke this verse:

> 23. That did vow the thane, on
> thing, if e'er he found me
> he would behead on sight the
> hapless maker of verses;
> yet he knew me not, though
> near enough the skald stood
> to the shatterer-of-shields; well
> shielded that disguise me!

15. Kenning for "head."

16. *Torráðr*, "Embarrassing."

17. It was believed that the king's good fortune could be transferred to the person on a mission from him.

18. A skerry is a submerged or half-submerged rock or islet.

19. Gaut is one of Ódin's names; the whole a kenning for "warrior."

20. Both the manner of telling and the substance of this and the following dreams is fairly stereotyped in the sagas; the soul of the dreamer leaves its body, traveling far and wide in search of things hidden. On its return the dreamer feels exhausted.

21. The open fire was at that time in the middle of the room, with no chimney. The smoke found its way out by the louver in the roof. This generally consisted of a movable panel covered with some translucent membrane. For a similar stratagem, cf. *Vatsdæla saga*, Chap. 28.

CHAPTER XXIV. THORMÓD AND SIGURD ATTACK LIÓT. THOR-
MÓD ESCAPES THORDÍS' PURSUIT AND SLAYS LIÓT. THOR-
MÓD REJOINS KING ÓLAF. THORMÓD'S DEATH AT STIK-
LASTAD

1. Opposite the high-seat. The nearer the door, the lower the rank of him who seats himself there.

2. *Ósvífr*, "bold, overbearing."

3. Literally, "everyone is (or acts) like his name."

4. The saga does not make clear just what was the trouble between them.

5. Where Gest was put up, cf. p. 146.

6. To be compared to a mare was the worst insult that could be offered a man.

7. Above (p. 146), he is called Thorgrím.

8. King Ólaf the Saint.

9. *Flateyarbók* more correctly has "three" winters'.

10. I.e., the son of Helga. From other sources it appears he was a cousin of Thorgeir.

11. The intimation seems to be that he fought with the king at Stiklastad.

12. "Arrow-combat" is a kenning for "battle"; its "urger," the "prince."

13. He sought refuge with high-born relatives in Russia.

14. A kenning for "fire."

15. According to *Flateyarbók* II, 338, and Snorri's *Heimskringla* (*Ólafs saga helga*, Chap. 205), this advice was given the king by Finn Arnason.

16. July 29, 1030.

17. For a full account of the *Bjarkamól* and the circumstances attending its recital here, cf. Axel Olrik, the *Heroic Legends of Denmark*, I, chaps. 2 and 3.

18. There is a double meaning in his words. He refers, of course, to lodgings in the Beyond.

19. Kennings for "battle."

20. Kenning for "sword"; its wielder, the "warrior."

21. Sigvat was absent on a pilgrimage to Rome; cf. Hollander *op.cit.*, p. 164.

22. These are prophetic words, for Sigvat became a mainstay and adviser to Ólaf's son, King Magnus. Cf. Hollander, *op.cit.*, p. 167f.

23. A kenning for "battle."

24. A kenning for "sword." This line would seem to contradict the statement made above that he had not received a wound till the fatal arrow pierced him.

25. Harold Sigurðarson was the king's half-brother. He made his escape from the battle, severely wounded, and ultimately ascended the throne. Cf. Hollander, *op.cit.*, p. 197.

26. Dag and his father, Ring, were relatives of the king who had fled with him out of Norway and on his return joined him with a force of some 1500 men. Cf. *Heimskringla, loc.cit.*, Chap. 199.

27. A kenning for "battle."

28. On the nature of these gurgling wounds, cf. a forthcoming article by Giddings and Magoun in *Révue Germanique*.

29. Toward the end of the battle Dag made a last fierce charge—known as "Dag's Fray"—in an attempt to change the outcome. See Appendix 3, p. 187.

NOTES ON APPENDICES

1. The northern Angelica (angelica sylvestris) is a large umbelliferous plant growing to a height of several feet, with a perennial root. Its fresh stalks have a somewhat bitter taste but are relished by many and used very much as celery is.

2. Chap. 50 of the *Grettis saga* tells of a number of somewhat apocryphal feats of strength by the three while together at Reykiaholt. And in Chap. 51, *ibid.*, Thorgils voices a similar opinion of their characters.

3. Canute the Great (?994-1035), enemy of Ólaf, was King of Denmark, England, and (for some time) of Norway.

4. Little is known about the life of Thórarin *loftunga* except that he was an Icelander and accompanied Canute the Great on his expedition against Norway in 1028. Snorri (*Heimskringla, Ólafs Saga helga*, Chap. 172) tells us that when the king learned that he had composed a *flokk* (short encomiastic poem) about him he was so enraged that he ordered the skald to have a *drápa* (longer encomiastic poem) about him ready the next day or be hanged; whereupon Thórarin changed it as desired. Of this poem, called his Head Ransom, only the refrain "Canute fends his kingdom as Greece's emperor doth heaven" is preserved. Two longer fragments prove him to have been a very skillful poet.

5. The functions of the *stafnbúi* are well described by Hárek. His was the most exposed position on the dragon ship, and he had to be both spokesman and leader.

6. The dragon Fáfnir, slain by Sigurd, brooded on his hoard. Hence the lair-of-Fáfnir is a kenning for "gold."

7. A kenning for "king."

8. The gift of poetry, which Ódin stole from the giants.

9. Certain favorable anchorages were reserved for the king; cf. Hollander, *op.cit.*, p. 180.

10. Or awnings, erected on the (undecked) ships for shelter.

11. This was the steersman's or commander's station, by the rudder.

12. Finn Arnason and Bishop Sigurd were staunch supporters of Ólaf. The former especially played a considerable role in the history of his times.

13. Kenning for "ships."

14. Kenning for "sword."

15. Kenning for "battle."

16. Kenning for "(generous) men."

17. "Hawk's-land" is a kenning for "arm" (which is the perch of the hunting falcon); its "oak," or tree, is a (rare) kenning for "woman."

18. A kenning for "battle."